Chapter 1
MCAT Basics

SO YOU WANT TO BE A DOCTOR

So...you want to be a doctor. If you're like most premeds, you've wanted to be a doctor since you were pretty young. When people asked you what you wanted to be when you grew up, you always answered "a doctor." You had toy medical kits, bandaged up your dog or cat, and played "hospital." You probably read your parents' home medical guides for fun.

When you got to high school you took the honors and AP classes. You studied hard, got straight A's (or at least really good grades!), and participated in extracurricular activities so you could get into a good college. And you succeeded!

At college you knew exactly what to do. You took your classes seriously, studied hard, and got a great GPA. You talked to your professors and hung out at office hours to get good letters of recommendation. You were a member of the premed society on campus, volunteered at hospitals, and shadowed doctors. All that's left to do now is get a good MCAT score.

Just the MCAT.

Just the most confidence-shattering, most demoralizing, longest, most brutal entrance exam for any graduate program. At about 7.5 hours (including breaks), the MCAT tops the list. Even the closest runners up, the LSAT and GMAT, are only about 4 hours long. The MCAT tests significant science content knowledge along with the ability to think quickly, reason logically, and read comprehensively, all under the pressure of a timed exam.

The path to a good MCAT score is not as easy to see as the path to a good GPA or the path to a good letter of recommendation. The MCAT is less about what you know, and more about how to apply what you know...and how to apply it quickly to new situations. Because the path might not be so clear, you might be worried. That's why you picked up this book.

We promise to demystify the MCAT for you, with clear descriptions of the different sections, how the test is scored, and what the test experience is like. We will help you understand general test-taking techniques as well as provide you with specific techniques for each section. We will review the science content you need to know as well as give you strategies for the Critical Analysis and Reasoning Skills (CARS) section. We'll show you the path to a good MCAT score and help you walk the path.

After all...you want to be a doctor. And we want you to succeed.

WHAT IS THE MCAT...REALLY?

Most test-takers approach the MCAT as though it were a typical college science test, one in which facts and knowledge simply need to be regurgitated in order to do well. They study for the MCAT the same way they did for their college tests, by memorizing facts and details, formulas and equations. And when they get to the MCAT they are surprised...and disappointed.

It's a myth that the MCAT is purely a content-knowledge test. If medical-school admission committees want to see what you know, all they have to do is look at your transcripts. What they really want to see is how you *think*, especially under pressure. *That's* what your MCAT score will tell them.

The MCAT is really a test of your ability to apply basic knowledge to different, possibly new, situations. It's a test of your ability to reason out and evaluate arguments. Do you still need to know your science content? Absolutely. But not at the level that most test-takers think they need to know it. Furthermore, your science knowledge won't help you on the Critical Analysis and Reasoning Skills (CARS) section. So how do you study for a test like this?

You study for the science sections by reviewing the basics and then applying them to MCAT practice questions. You study for the CARS section by learning how to adapt your existing reading and analytical skills to the nature of the test (more information about the CARS section can be found in the *MCAT Critical Analysis and Reasoning Skills Review*).

The book you are holding will review all the relevant MCAT General Chemistry content you will need for the test, and a little bit more. It includes hundreds of questions designed to make you think about the material in a deeper way, along with full explanations to clarify the logical thought process needed to get to the answer. It also comes with access to three full-length online practice exams to further hone your skills. For more information on accessing those online exams, please refer to the "Register Your Book Online!" spread on page x.

MCAT NUTS AND BOLTS

Overview

The MCAT is a computer-based test (CBT) that is *not* adaptive. Adaptive tests base your next question on whether or not you've answered the current question correctly. The MCAT is *linear*, or *fixed-form*, meaning that the questions are in a predetermined order and do not change based on your answers. However, there are many versions of the test, so that on a given test day, different people will see different versions. The following table highlights the features of the MCAT exam.

Registration	Online via www.aamc.org. Begins as early as six months prior to test date; available up until week of test (subject to seat availability).
Testing Centers	Administered at small, secure, climate-controlled computer testing rooms.
Security	Photo ID with signature, electronic fingerprint, electronic signature verification, assigned seat.
Proctoring	None. Test administrator checks examinee in and assigns seat at computer. All testing instructions are given on the computer.
Frequency of Test	Many times per year distributed over January, April, May, June, July, August, and September.
Format	Exclusively computer-based. NOT an adaptive test.
Length of Test Day	7.5 hours
Breaks	Optional 10-minute breaks between sections, with a 30-minute break for lunch.
Section Names	1. Chemical and Physical Foundations of Biological Systems (Chem/Phys) 2. Critical Analysis and Reasoning Skills (CARS) 3. Biological and Biochemical Foundations of Living Systems (Bio/Biochem) 4. Psychological, Social, and Biological Foundations of Behavior (Psych/Soc)
Number of Questions and Timing	59 Chem/Phys questions, 95 minutes 53 CARS questions, 90 minutes 59 Bio/Biochem questions, 95 minutes 59 Psych/Soc questions, 95 minutes
Scoring	Test is scaled. Several forms per administration.
Allowed/Not allowed	No timers/watches. Noise reduction headphones available. Scratch paper and pencils given at start of test and taken at end of test. Locker or secure area provided for personal items.
Results: Timing and Delivery	Approximately 30 days. Electronic scores only, available online through AAMC login. Examinees can print official score reports.
Maximum Number of Retakes	As of April 2015, the MCAT can be taken a maximum of three times in one year, four times over two years, and seven times over the lifetime of the examinee. An examinee can be registered for only one date at a time.

Registration

Registration for the exam is completed online at https://www.aamc.org/students/applying/mcat/reserving. The AAMC opens registration for a given test date at least two months in advance of the date, often earlier. It's a good idea to register well in advance of your desired test date to make sure that you get a seat.

Sections

There are four sections on the MCAT exam: Chemical and Physical Foundations of Biological Systems (Chem/Phys), Critical Analysis and Reasoning Skills (CARS), Biological and Biochemical Foundations of Living Systems (Bio/Biochem), and Psychological, Social, and Biological Foundations of Behavior (Psych/Soc). All sections consist of multiple-choice questions.

Section	Concepts Tested	Number of Questions and Timing
Chemical and Physical Foundations of Biological Systems	Basic concepts in chemistry and physics, including biochemistry; scientific inquiry; reasoning; research methods; and statistics.	59 questions, 95 minutes
Critical Analysis and Reasoning Skills	Critical analysis of information drawn from a wide range of social science and humanities disciplines.	53 questions, 90 minutes
Biological and Biochemical Foundations of Living Systems	Basic concepts in biology and biochemistry, scientific inquiry, reasoning, research methods, and statistics.	59 questions, 95 minutes
Psychological, Social, and Biological Foundations of Behavior	Basic concepts in psychology, sociology, and biology, scientific inquiry, reasoning, research methods, and statistics.	59 questions, 95 minutes

Most questions on the MCAT (44 in the science sections, all 53 in the CARS section) are **passage-based**; the science sections have 10 passages each and the CARS section has 9. A passage consists of a few paragraphs of information on which several following questions are based. In the science sections, passages often include equations or reactions, tables, graphs, figures, and experiments to analyze. CARS passages come from literature in the social sciences, humanities, ethics, philosophy, cultural studies, and population health, and do not test content knowledge in any way.

Some questions in the science sections are *freestanding questions* (FSQs). These questions are independent of any passage information and appear in several groups of about four to five questions, interspersed throughout the passages. 15 of the questions in the sciences sections are freestanding, and the remainder are passage-based.

Each section on the MCAT is separated by either a 10-minute break or a 30-minute lunch break:

Section	Time
Test Center Check-In	Variable, can take up to 40 minutes if center is busy.
Tutorial	10 minutes
Chemical and Physical Foundations of Biological Systems	95 minutes
Break	10 minutes
Critical Analysis and Reasoning Skills	90 minutes
Lunch Break	30 minutes
Biological and Biochemical Foundations of Living Systems	95 minutes
Break	10 minutes
Psychological, Social, and Biological Foundations of Behavior	95 minutes
Void Option	5 minutes
Survey	5 minutes

The survey includes questions about your satisfaction with the overall MCAT experience, including registration, check-in, etc., as well as questions about how you prepared for the test.

Scoring

The MCAT is a scaled exam, meaning that your raw score will be converted into a scaled score that takes into account the difficulty of the questions. There is no guessing penalty. All sections are scored from 118-132, with a total scaled score range of 472-528. Because different versions of the test have varying levels of difficulty, the scale will be different from one exam to the next. Thus, there is no "magic number" of questions to get right in order to get a particular score. Plus, some of the questions on the test are considered "experimental" and do not count toward your score; they are just there to be evaluated for possible future inclusion in a test.

At the end of the test (after you complete the Psychological, Social, and Biological Foundations of Behavior section), you will be asked to choose one of the following two options, "I wish to have my MCAT exam scored" or "I wish to VOID my MCAT exam." You have five minutes to make a decision, and if you do not select one of the options in that time, the test will automatically be scored. If you choose the VOID option, your test will not be scored (you will not now, or ever, get a numerical score for this test), medical schools will not know you took the test, and no refunds will be granted. You cannot "unvoid" your scores at a later time.

So, what's a good score? The AAMC is centering the scale at 500 (i.e., 500 will be the 50th percentile), and recommends that application committees consider applicants near the center of the range. To be on the safe side, aim for a total score of around 510. Remember that if your GPA is on the low side, you'll need higher MCAT scores to compensate, and if you have a strong GPA, you can get away with lower MCAT scores. But the reality is that your chances of acceptance depend on a lot more than just your MCAT scores. It's a combination of your GPA, your MCAT scores, your undergraduate coursework, letters of recommendation, experience related to the medical field (such as volunteer work or research), extracurricular activities, your personal statement, etc. Medical schools are looking for a complete package, not just good scores and a good GPA.

GENERAL LAYOUT AND TEST-TAKING STRATEGIES

Layout of the Test

In each section of the test, the computer screen is divided vertically, with the passage on the left and the range of questions for that passage indicated above (such as "Passage 1, Questions 1–5"). The scroll bar for the passage text appears in the middle of the screen. Each question appears on the right, and you need to click "Next" to move to each subsequent question.

In the science sections, the freestanding questions are found in groups of 4–5, interspersed with the passages. The screen is still divided vertically; on the left is the statement "Questions [X–XX] do not refer to a passage and are independent of each other" and each question appears on the right as described above.

CBT Tools

There are a number of tools available on the test, including highlighting, strike-outs, the Mark button, the Review button, the Periodic Table button, and of course, scratch paper. The following is a brief description of each tool.

1) **Highlighting:** This is done in the passage text (including table entries and some equations, but excluding figures and molecular structures) and in the question stems by left-clicking and dragging the mouse across the words you wish to highlight; the selected words will then be highlighted in blue. When you release the mouse, a highlighting icon will appear; clicking on the icon will highlight the selected text in yellow. To remove the highlighting, left-click on the highlighted text.
2) **Strike-outs:** Right-clicking on an answer choice causes the entire text of that choice to be crossed out. The strike-out can be removed by right-clicking again. Left-clicking selects an answer choice; note than an answer choice that is selected cannot be struck out. When you strike out a figure or molecular structure, instead of being crossed out, the image turns grey.
3) **Mark button:** This allows you to flag the question for later review. When clicked, the flag on the "Mark" button turns red and says "Marked."
4) **Review button:** Clicking this button brings up a new screen showing all questions and their status (either "completed," "incomplete," or "marked"). You can choose to: "review all," "review incomplete," or "review marked." You can also double-click any question number to quickly return to that specific question. You can only review questions in the section of the MCAT you are currently taking, but the Review button can be clicked at any time during the allotted time for that section; you do NOT have to wait until the end of the section to click it.
5) **Periodic Table button:** Clicking this button will open a periodic table. Note that the periodic table is large, however it can be resized to see the questions and a portion of the periodic table at the same time.
6) **Scratch paper:** You will be given four pages (8 faces) of scratch paper at the start of the test. You can ask for more at any point during the test, and your first set of paper will be collected before you receive fresh paper. Scratch paper is only useful if it is kept organized; do not give in to the tendency to write on the first available open space! Good organization will be very helpful when/if you wish to review a question. Indicate the passage number and the range of questions for that passage in a box near the top of your scratch work, and indicate the question you are working on in a circle to the left of the notes for that question. Draw a line under your scratch work when you change passages to keep the work separate. Do not erase or scribble over any previous work. If you do not think it is correct, draw one line through the work and start again. You may have already done some useful work without realizing it.

General Strategy for the Science Sections

Passages vs. FSQs in the Science Sections: What to Start With

Since the questions are displayed on separate screens, it is awkward and time consuming to click through all of the questions up front to find the FSQs. Therefore, go through the section on a first pass and decide whether to do the passage now or to save it for later, basing your decision on the passage text and the first question. Tackle the FSQs as you come upon them. More details are below.

Here is an outline of the procedure:

1) For each passage, write a heading on your scratch paper with the passage number, the general topic, and its range of questions (e.g. "Passage 1, thermodynamics, Q 1–5" or "Passage 2, enzymes, Q 6–9). The passage numbers do not currently appear in the Review screen, thus having the question numbers on your scratch paper will allow you to move through the section more efficiently.
2) Skim the text and rank the passage. If a passage is a "Now," complete it before moving on to the next passage (also see "Attacking the Questions" below). If it is a "Later" passage, first write "SKIPPED" in block letters under the passage heading on your scratch paper and leave room for your work when you come back to complete that passage. (Note that the specific passages you skip will be unique to you; in the Bio/Biochem section, you might choose to do all Biology passages first, then come back for Biochemistry. Or in Chem/Phys you might choose to skip experiment-based or analytical passages. Know ahead of time what type of passage you are going to skip and follow your plan.)
3) Next, click on the "Review" button at the bottom to get to the review screen. Double-click on the first question of the next passage; you'll be able to identify it because you know the range of questions from the passage you just skipped. This will take you to the next passage, where you will repeat steps 1–3.
4) Once you have completed the "Now" passages, go to the review screen and double-click the first question for the first passage you skipped. Answer the questions, and continue going back to the review screen and repeating this procedure for other passages you have skipped.

Attacking the Questions

As you work through the questions, if you encounter a particularly lengthy question, or a question that requires a lot of analysis, you may choose to skip it. This is a wise strategy because it ensures you will tackle all the easier questions first, the ones you are more likely to get right. If you choose to skip the question (or if you attempt it but get stuck), write down the question number on your scratch paper, click the Mark button to flag the question in the Review screen, and move on to the next question. At the end of the passage, click back through the set of questions to complete any that you skipped over the first time through, and make sure that you have filled in an answer for every question.

General Strategy for the CARS Section

Ranking and Ordering the Passages: What to Start With

Ranking: Since the questions are displayed on separate screens, it is awkward and time consuming to click through all of the questions before ranking each passage as Now (an easier passage), Later (a harder passage), or Killer (a passage that you will randomly guess on). Therefore, rank the passage and decide whether or not to do it on the first pass through the section based on the passage text, skimming the first 2–3 sentences.

Ordering: Because of the additional clicking through screens (or, use of the Review screen) that is required to navigate through the section, the "Two-Pass" system (completing the "Now" passages as you find them) is likely to be your most efficient approach. However, if you find that you are continuously making a lot of bad ranking decisions, it is still valid to experiment with the "Three-Pass" approach (ranking all nine passages up front before attempting your first "Now" passage).

Here is an outline of the basic Ranking and Ordering procedure to follow.

1) For each passage, write a heading on your scratch paper with the passage number and its range of questions (e.g. "Passage 1, Q 1–7). The passage numbers do not currently appear in the Review screen, thus having the question numbers on your scratch paper will allow you to move through the section more efficiently.
2) Skim the first 2–3 sentences and rank the passage. If the passage is a "Now," complete it before moving on to the next. If it is a "Later" or "Killer," first write either "Later" or "Killer" and "SKIPPED" in block letters under the passage heading on your scratch paper and leave room for your work if you decide to come back and complete that passage. Then click through each question, marking each one and filling in random guesses, until you get to the next passage.
3) Once you have completed the "Now" passages, come back for your second pass and complete the "Later" passages, leaving your random guesses in place for any "Killer" passages that you choose not to complete. Go to the Review screen and use your scratch paper notes on the question numbers. Double-click on the number of the first question for that passage to go back to that question, and proceed from there. Alternatively, if you have consistently marked all the questions for passages you skipped in your first pass you can use "Review Marked" from the Review screen to find and complete your "Later" passages.
4) Regardless of how you choose to find your second pass passages, unmark each question after you complete it, so that you can continue to rely on the Review screen (and the "Review Marked" function") to identify questions that you have not yet attempted.

Previewing the Questions

The formatting and functioning of the tools facilitates effective previewing. Having each question on a separate screen will encourage you to really focus on that question. Even more importantly, you can now highlight in the question stem (but not in the answer choices).

Here is the basic procedure for previewing the questions:

1) Start with the first question, and if it has lead words referencing passage content, highlight them. You may also choose to jot them down on your scratch paper. Once you reach and preview the last question for the set on that passage, THEN stay on that screen and work the passage (your highlighting appears and stays on every passage screen, and persists through the whole 90 minutes).
2) Once you have worked the passage and defined the Bottom Line—the main idea and tone of the entire passage—work **backward** from the last question to the first. If you skip over any questions as you go (see "Attacking the Questions" below), write down the question number on your scratch paper. Then click **forward** through the set of questions, completing any that you skipped over the first time through. Once you reach and complete the last question for that passage, clicking "Next" will send you to the first question of the next passage. Working the questions from last to first the first time through the set will eliminate the need to click back through multiple screens to get to the first question immediately after previewing, and will also make it easier and more efficient to do the hardest questions last (see "Attacking the Questions" below).

Attacking the Questions

The question types and the procedure for actually attacking each type will be discussed later. However, it is still important **not** to attempt the hardest questions first (potentially getting stuck, wasting time, and discouraging yourself).

So, as you work the questions from last to first (see "Previewing the Questions" above), if you encounter a particularly difficult and/or lengthy question (or if you attempt a question but get stuck) write down the question number on your scratch paper (you may also choose to mark it) and move on backward to the next question. Then click **forward** through the set and complete any that you skipped over the first time through the set, unmarking any questions that you marked that first time through and making sure that you have filled in an answer for every question.

Pacing Strategy for the MCAT

Since the MCAT is a timed test, you must keep an eye on the timer and adjust your pacing as necessary. It would be terrible to run out of time at the end to discover that the last few questions could have been easily answered in just a few seconds each.

In the science sections you will have about one minute and thirty-five seconds (1:35) per question, and in the CARS section you will have about one minute and forty seconds (1:40) per question (not taking into account time spent reading the passage before answering the questions).

Section	# of Questions in passage	Approximate time (including reading the passage)
Chem/Phys, Bio/Biochem, and Psych/Soc	4	6.5 minutes
	5	8 minutes
	6	9.5 minutes
CARS	5	8.5 minutes
	6	10 minutes
	7	11.5 minutes

When starting a passage in the science sections, make note of how much time you will allot for it, and the starting time on the timer. Jot down on your scratch paper what the timer should say at the end of the passage. Then just keep an eye on it as you work through the questions. If you are near the end of the time for that passage, guess on any remaining questions, make some notes on your scratch paper, Mark the questions, and move on. Come back to those questions if you have time.

For the CARS section, keep in mind that many people will maximize their score by *not* trying to complete every question or every passage in the section. A good strategy for test takers who cannot achieve a high level of accuracy on all nine passages is to randomly guess on at least one passage in the section, and spend your time getting a high percentage of the other questions right. To complete all nine CARS passages, you have about ten minutes per passage. To complete eight of the nine, you have about 11 minutes per passage.

To help maximize your number of correct answer choices in any section, do the questions and passages within that section in the order *you* want to do them in. See "General Strategy" above.

Process of Elimination

Process of elimination (POE) is probably the most useful technique you have to tackle MCAT questions. Since there is no guessing penalty, POE allows you to increase your probability of choosing the correct answer by eliminating those you are sure are wrong.

1) Strike out any choices that you are sure are incorrect or that do not address the issue raised in the question.
2) Jot down some notes to help clarify your thoughts if you return to the question.
3) Use the "Mark" button to flag the question for review. (Note, however, that in the CARS section, you generally should not be returning to rethink questions once you have moved on to a new passage.)
4) Do not leave it blank! For the sciences, if you are not sure and you have already spent more than 60 seconds on that question, just pick one of the remaining choices. If you have time to review it at the end, you can always debate the remaining choices based on your previous notes. For CARS, if you have been through the choices two or three times, have re-read the question stem and gone back to the passage, and you are still stuck, move on. Do the remaining questions for that passage, take one more look at the question you were stuck on, then pick an answer and move on for good.
5) Special Note: if three of the four answer choices have been eliminated, the remaining choice must be the correct answer. Don't waste time pondering *why* it is correct, just click it and move on. The MCAT doesn't care if you truly understand why it's the right answer, only that you have the right answer selected.
6) More subject-specific information on techniques will be presented in the next chapter.

Guessing

Remember, there is NO guessing penalty on the MCAT. NEVER leave a question blank!

QUESTION TYPES

In the science sections of the MCAT, the questions fall into one of three main categories.

1) Memory questions: These questions can be answered directly from prior knowledge and represent about 25 percent of the total number of questions.
2) Explicit questions: These questions are those for which the answer is explicitly stated in the passage. To answer them correctly, for example, may just require finding a definition, or reading a graph, or making a simple connection. Explicit questions represent about 35 percent of the total number of questions.
3) Implicit questions: These questions require you to apply knowledge to a new situation; the answer is typically implied by the information in the passage. These questions often start "if.... then...." (for example, "if we modify the experiment in the passage like this, then what result would we expect?"). Implicit style questions make up about 40 percent of the total number of questions.

In the CARS section, the questions fall into four main categories:

1) Specific questions: These either ask you for facts from the passage (Retrieval questions) or require you to deduce what is most likely to be true based on the passage (Inference questions).
2) General questions: These ask you to summarize themes (Main Idea and Primary Purpose questions) or evaluate an author's opinion (Tone/Attitude questions).
3) Reasoning questions: These ask you to describe the purpose of, or the support provided for, a statement made in the passage (Structure questions) or to judge how well the author supports his or her argument (Evaluate questions).

4) Application questions: These ask you to apply new information from either the question stem itself (New Information questions) or from the answer choices (Strengthen, Weaken, and Analogy questions) to the passage.

More detail on question types and strategies can be found in Chapter 2.

TESTING TIPS

Before Test Day

- Take a trip to the test center at least a day or two before your actual test date so that you can easily find the building and room on test day. This will also allow you to gauge traffic and see if you need money for parking or anything like that. Knowing this type of information ahead of time will greatly reduce your stress on the day of your test.
- During the week before the test, adjust your sleeping schedule so that you are going to bed and getting up in the morning at the same times as on the day before and morning of the MCAT. Prioritize getting a reasonable amount of sleep during the last few nights before the test.
- Don't do any heavy studying the day before the test. This is not a test you can cram for! Your goal at this point is to rest and relax so that you can go into test day in a good physical and mental condition.
- Eat well. Try to avoid excessive caffeine and sugar. Ideally, in the weeks leading up to the actual test you should experiment a little bit with foods and practice tests to see which foods give you the most endurance. Aim for steady blood sugar levels during the test: sports drinks, peanut-butter crackers, trail mix, etc. make good snacks for your breaks and lunch.

General Test Day Info and Tips

- On the day of the test, arrive at the test center at least a half hour prior to the start time of your test.
- Examinees will be checked in to the center in the order in which they arrive.
- You will be assigned a locker or secure area in which to put your personal items. Textbooks and study notes are not allowed, so there is no need to bring them with you to the test center.
- Your ID will be checked, a digital image of your fingerprint will be taken, and you will be asked to sign in.
- You will be given scratch paper and a couple of pencils, and the test center administrator will take you to the computer on which you will complete the test. You may not choose a computer; you must use the computer assigned to you.
- Nothing, not even your watch, is allowed at the computer station except your photo ID, your locker key (if provided), and a factory sealed packet of ear plugs.
- If you choose to leave the testing room at the breaks, you will have your fingerprint checked again, and you will have to sign in and out.
- You are allowed to access the items in your locker, except for notes and cell phones. (Check your test center's policy on cell phones ahead of time; some centers do not even allow them to be kept in your locker.)
- Don't forget to bring the snack foods and lunch you experimented with in your practice tests.
- At the end of the test, the test administrator will collect your scratch paper and shred it.
- Definitely take the breaks! Get up and walk around. It's a good way to clear your head between sections and get the blood (and oxygen!) flowing to your brain.
- Ask for new scratch paper at the breaks if you use it all up.

Chapter 2
General Chemistry Strategy for the MCAT

2.1 SCIENCE SECTIONS OVERVIEW

There are three science sections on the MCAT:

- Chemical and Physical Foundations of Biological Systems
- Biological and Biochemical Foundations of Living Systems
- Psychological, Social, and Biological Foundations of Behavior

The Chemical and Physical Foundations of Biological Systems section (Chem/Phys) is the first section on the test. It includes questions from General Chemistry (about 30%), Physics (about 25%), Organic Chemistry (about 15%), Biochemistry (about 25%), and Biology (about 5%). Further, the questions often test chemical and physical concepts within a biological setting, for example, pressure and fluid flow in blood vessels. A solid grasp of math fundamentals is required (arithmetic, algebra, graphs, trigonometry, vectors, proportions, and logarithms), however there are no calculus-based questions.

The Biological and Biochemical Foundations of Living Systems section (Bio/Biochem) is the third section on the test. Approximately 65% of the questions in this section come from biology, approximately 25% come from biochemistry, and approximately 10% come from Organic and General Chemistry. Math calculations are generally not required on this section of the test, however a basic understanding of statistics as used in biological research is helpful.

The Psychological, Social, and Biological Foundations of Behavior section (Psych/Soc) is the fourth and final section on the test. About 60% of the questions will be drawn from Psychology, about 30% from Sociology, and about 10% from Biology. As with the Bio/Biochem section, calculations are generally not required, however a basic understanding of statistics as used in research is helpful.

Most of the questions in the science sections (44 of the 59) are passage-based, and each section has ten passages. Passages consist of a few paragraphs of information and include equations, reactions, graphs, figures, tables, experiments, and data. Four to six questions will be associated with each passage.

The remaining 25% of the questions (15 of 59) in each science section are freestanding questions (FSQs). These questions appear in approximately four groups interspersed between the passages. Each group contains four to five questions.

95 minutes are allotted to each of the science sections. This breaks down to approximately one minute and 35 seconds per question.

2.2 GENERAL SCIENCE PASSAGE TYPES

The passages in the science sections fall into one of three main categories: Information and/or Situation Presentation, Experiment/Research Presentation, or Persuasive Reasoning.

Information and/or Situation Presentation

These passages either present straightforward scientific information or they describe a particular event or occurrence. Generally, questions associated with these passages test basic science facts or ask you to predict outcomes given new variables or new information. Here is an example of an Information/Situation Presentation passage:

Figure 1 shows a portion of the inner mechanism of a typical home smoke detector. It consists of a pair of capacitor plates which are charged by a 9-volt battery (not shown). The capacitor plates (electrodes) are connected to a sensor device, D; the resistor R denotes the internal resistance of the sensor. Normally, air acts as an insulator and no current would flow in the circuit shown. However, inside the smoke detector is a small sample of an artificially produced radioactive element, americium-241, which decays primarily by emitting alpha particles, with a half-life of approximately 430 years. The daughter nucleus of the decay has a half-life in excess of two million years and therefore poses virtually no biohazard.

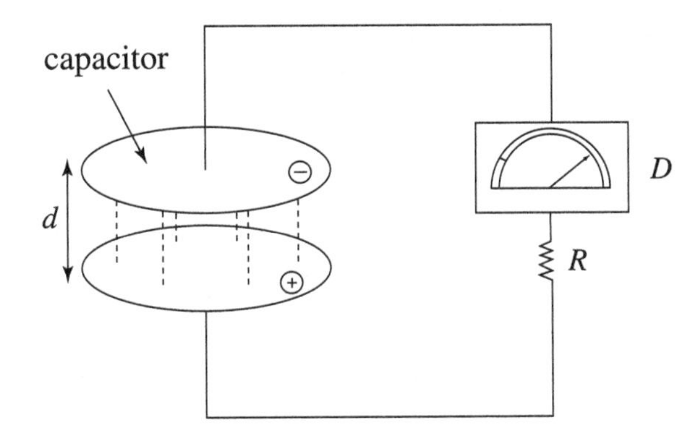

Figure 1 Smoke detector mechanism

The decay products (alpha particles and gamma rays) from the ^{241}Am sample ionize air molecules between the plates and thus provide a conducting pathway which allows current to flow in the circuit shown in Figure 1. A steady-state current is quickly established and remains as long as the battery continues to maintain a 9-volt potential difference between its terminals. However, if smoke particles enter the space between the capacitor plates and thereby interrupt the flow, the current is reduced, and the sensor responds to this change by triggering the alarm. (Furthermore, as the battery starts to "die out," the resulting drop in current is also detected to alert the homeowner to replace the battery.)

$$C = \varepsilon_0 \frac{A}{d}$$

Equation 1

where ε_0 is the universal permittivity constant, equal to 8.85×10^{-12} $C^2/(N\ m^2)$. Since the area A of each capacitor plate in the smoke detector is 20 cm^2 and the plates are separated by a distance d of 5 mm, the capacitance is 3.5×10^{-12} F = 3.5 pF.

Experiment/Research Presentation

These passages present the details of experiments and research procedures. They often include data tables and graphs. Generally, questions associated with these passages ask you to interpret data, draw conclusions, and make inferences. Here is an example of an Experiment/Research Presentation passage:

The development of sexual characteristics depends upon various factors, the most important of which are hormonal control, environmental stimuli, and the genetic makeup of the individual. The hormones that contribute to the development include the steroid hormones estrogen, progesterone, and testosterone, as well as the pituitary hormones FSH (follicle-stimulating hormone) and LH (luteinizing hormone).

To study the mechanism by which estrogen exerts its effects, a researcher performed the following experiments using cell culture assays.

Experiment 1:

Human embryonic placental mesenchyme (HEPM) cells were grown for 48 hours in Dulbecco's Modified Eagle Medium (DMEM), with media change every 12 hours. Upon confluent growth, cells were exposed to a 10 mg per mL solution of green fluorescent-labeled estrogen for 1 hour. Cells were rinsed with DMEM and observed under confocal fluorescent microscopy.

Experiment 2:

HEPM cells were grown to confluence as in Experiment 1. Cells were exposed to Pesticide A for 1 hour, followed by the 10 mg/mL solution of labeled estrogen, rinsed as in Experiment 1, and observed under confocal fluorescent microscopy.

Experiment 3:

Experiment 1 was repeated with Chinese Hamster Ovary (CHO) cells instead of HEPM cells.

Experiment 4:

CHO cells injected with cytoplasmic extracts of HEPM cells were grown to confluence, exposed to the 10 mg/mL solution of labeled estrogen for 1 hour, and observed under confocal fluorescent microscopy.

The results of these experiments are given in Table 1.

Table 1 Detection of Estrogen (+ indicates presence of Estrogen)

Experiment	Media	Cytoplasm	Nucleus
1	+	+	+
2	+	+	+
3	+	+	+
4	+	+	+

After observing the cells in each experiment, the researcher bathed the cells in a solution containing 10 mg per mL of a red fluorescent probe that binds specifically to the estrogen receptor only when its active site is occupied. After 1 hour, the cells were rinsed with DMEM and observed under confocal fluorescent microscopy. The results are presented in Table 2.

The researcher also repeated Experiment 2 using Pesticide B, an estrogen analog, instead of Pesticide A. Results from other researchers had shown that Pesticide B binds to the active site of the cytosolic estrogen receptor (with an affinity 10,000 times greater than that of estrogen) and causes increased transcription of mRNA.

Table 2 Observed Fluorescence and Estrogen Effects (G = green, R = red)

Experiment	Media	Cytoplasm	Nucleus	Estrogen effects observed?
1	G only	G and R	G and R	Yes
2	G only	G only	G only	No
3	G only	G only	G only	No
4	G only	G and R	G and R	Yes

Based on these results, the researcher determined that estrogen had no effect when not bound to a cytosolic, estrogen-specific receptor.

Persuasive Reasoning

These passages typically present a scientific phenomenon along with a hypothesis that explains the phenomenon, and may include counter-arguments as well. Questions associated with these passages ask you to evaluate the hypothesis or arguments. Persuasive Reasoning passages in the science sections of the MCAT tend to be less common than Information Presentation or Experiment-based passages. Here is an example of a Persuasive Reasoning passage:

Two theoretical chemists attempted to explain the observed trends of acidity by applying two interpretations of molecular orbital theory. Consider the pK_a values of some common acids listed along the conjugate base:

acid	pK_a	conjugate base
H_2SO_4	< 0	HSO_4^-
H_2CrO_4	5.0	$HCrO_4^-$
H_2PO_4	2.1	$H_2PO_4^-$
HF	3.9	F^-
HOCl	7.8	ClO^-
HCN	9.5	CN^-
HIO_3	1.2	IO_3^-

Recall that acids with a pK_a < 0 are called strong acids, and those with a pK_a > 0 are called weak acids. The arguments of the chemists are given below.

Chemist #1:

"The acidity of a compound is proportional to the polarization of the H—X bond, where X is some nonmetal element. Complex acids, such as H_2SO_4, $HClO_4$, and HNO_3 are strong acids because the H—O bonding electrons are strongly drawn towards the oxygen. It is generally true that a covalent bond weakens as its polarization increases. Therefore, one can conclude that the strength of an acid is proportional to the number of electronegative atoms in that acid."

Chemist #2:

"The acidity of a compound is proportional to the number of stable resonance structures of that acid's conjugate base. H_2SO_4, $HClO_4$, and HNO_3 are all strong acids because their respective conjugate bases exhibit a high degree of resonance stabilization."

MAPPING A PASSAGE

"Mapping a passage" refers to the combination of on-screen highlighting and scratch paper notes that you take while working through a passage. Typically, good things to highlight include the overall topic of a paragraph, unfamiliar terms, unusual terms, italicized terms, numerical values, hypotheses, and experimental results. Scratch paper notes can be used to summarize the paragraphs and to jot down important facts and connections that are made when reading the passage. More details on passage mapping will be presented in Section 2.5.

2.3 GENERAL SCIENCE QUESTION TYPES

Questions in the science sections are generally one of three main types: Memory, Explicit, or Implicit.

Memory Questions

These questions can be answered directly from prior knowledge, with no need to reference the passage or question text. Memory questions represent approximately 25 percent of the science questions on the MCAT. Usually, Memory questions are found as FSQs, but they can also be tucked into a passage. Here's an example of a Memory question:

Which of the following acetylating conditions will convert diethylamine into an amide at the fastest rate?

A) Acetic acid/HCl
B) Acetic anhydride
C) Acetyl chloride
D) Ethyl acetate

Explicit Questions

Explicit questions can be answered primarily with information from the passage, along with prior knowledge. They may require data retrieval, graph analysis, or making a simple connection. Explicit questions make up approximately 35–40 percent of the science questions on the MCAT; here's an example (taken from the Information/Situation Presentation passage above):

The sensor device D shown in Figure 1 performs its function by acting as:

A) an ohmmeter.
B) a voltmeter.
C) a potentiometer.
D) an ammeter.

Implicit Questions

These questions require you to take information from the passage, combine it with your prior knowledge, apply it to a new situation, and come to some logical conclusion. They typically require more complex connections than do Explicit questions, and may also require data retrieval, graph analysis, etc. Implicit questions usually require a solid understanding of the passage information. They make up approximately 35–40 percent of the science questions on the MCAT; here's an example (taken from the Experiment/Research Presentation passage above):

If Experiment 2 were repeated, but this time exposing the cells first to Pesticide A and then to Pesticide B before exposing them to the green fluorescent-labeled estrogen and the red fluorescent probe, which of the following statements will most likely be true?

A) Pesticide A and Pesticide B bind to the same site on the estrogen receptor.
B) Estrogen effects would be observed.
C) Only green fluorescence would be observed.
D) Both green and red fluorescence would be observed.

The Rod of Asclepius

You may notice this Rod of Asclepius icon as you read through the book. In Greek mythology, the Rod of Asclepius is associated with healing and medicine; the symbol continues to be used today to represent medicine and healthcare. You won't see this on the actual MCAT, but we've used it here to call attention to medically related examples and questions.

2.4 GENERAL CHEMISTRY ON THE MCAT

Although general chemistry is sometimes remembered as a daunting topic from college, the MCAT does not test the fine details of general chemistry. Rather, the focus of this section is on having a strong knowledge of chemistry fundamentals, and manipulating that knowledge to adapt to different scenarios presented in passages and questions. The passages often contain information that recapitulates basic chemistry knowledge, and may present additional information that builds on fundamental concepts.

The majority of the G-Chem questions will not be based on rote memory, but will require you to retrieve information from the passage and use some deductive reasoning skills. Thus, in order to succeed in this section, you not only need solid knowledge of fundamental principles of chemistry, but also strong critical reasoning and reading comprehension skills. These three components may be stressed differently depending on the passage type.

The science sections of the MCAT have 10 passages and 15 freestanding questions (FSQs). General Chemistry will make up about a third of the questions in the Chemical and Physical Foundations of Biological Systems section. The remaining questions will be on Physics (25%), Organic Chemistry (15%), and Biochemistry (25%). In addition, about 5% of the questions on the Biological and Biochemical Foundations of Living Systems section will be General Chemistry.

2.5 PASSAGE TYPES AS THEY APPLY TO GENERAL CHEMISTRY

Information/Situation Presentation: G-Chem

These passages assume knowledge of basic scientific concepts, and also present new information that builds on these basic concepts. The new information may be presented in a way that is very similar to how it would appear in a textbook or other scientific reference. The questions may be about basic scientific facts that you already know, but often the passage will present topics or subtopics with which you are unfamiliar. Information/Situation Presentation passages can be intimidating, as they often explore topics in a greater level of detail than the scope of your MCAT preparation. However, keep in mind that the whole point of these types of passages is to force you to use critical reasoning and apply your basic scientific knowledge to new topics. It is not to see how much advanced scientific coursework you have memorized. Therefore, it is important when you see a passage on, say, molecular orbital theory, that you don't think to yourself, "Oh no!! I forgot to study molecular orbital theory!!!" Rather, look at the information in the passage, and consider how your knowledge about more basic chemical concepts, such as electron configurations, can be applied in order to answer the questions. The new information in the passage can supplement your basic knowledge.

This type of passage may also present information in the context of a specific situation, such as the results of a research study or an experiment. In this case, the questions may ask you to distinguish between data that supports or refutes the result being presented. In some passages, an apparently contradictory or erroneous result is presented and questions may ask what mistakes could have been made over the course of the experiment to cause such a result. Thus, these passages require to you think critically about the importance of each chemical and physical element of an experiment. Note however, that they do not present the steps of an experiment in great detail; that style is reserved for Experiment/Research Presentation passages.

Experiment/Research Presentation: G-Chem

These passages present an experimental set up in great detail; they describe the rationale behind an experiment, how it is set up and executed, and its results. In these passages you are often asked to analyze data given in the form of charts and graphs. In addition, questions may ask you how the results of the experiment would differ if a certain variable were changed; this requires you to think critically about the role of each element of the experiment. In this passage type, be careful not to gloss over important experimental details as you retrieve information from the passage. Be aware that details such as units can make the difference between answering a question correctly or incorrectly, and be vigilant about these experimental details as you work through the questions and look back to the passage.

Persuasive Argument: G-Chem

In a Persuasive Argument passage, two perspectives on a problem are presented. It may be different researchers putting forth two different methodologies for conducting an experiment, or two different explanations for an experimental result or phenomenon.

The questions may ask how the authors came to develop different perspectives, or ask you to evaluate the credibility of each of their arguments. Persuasive Argument passages are the least common passage type in G-Chem.

READING A GENERAL CHEMISTRY PASSAGE

Reading a G-Chem passage is not like reading a scientific paper or a textbook. That is, you are not reading thoroughly and trying to understand the relevance of each sentence, as the passage will likely contain details beyond the scope of the questions.

Instead, your goal is to take no more than 60 seconds and skim the passage in order to determine the general topic area being tested and create a brief passage map before moving on to the questions. To do this as efficiently as possible, focus on the first sentence of each paragraph and any bolded or italicized words. In addition, chemical equations and figures may provide insight as to the general topic of the passage. For example, if you see a titration curve, it is likely that the passage will test acid-base chemistry.

G-Chem passages often include complex graphs and data tables. Avoid the temptation to analyze this data on your first pass through the passage. Rather, wait until you find a question that requires the use of the data in the graph or table, then analyze the data in the context of that question. This approach is more efficient and productive than trying to preemptively interpret data.

The bottom line: You can always go back and reread more details from the passage. Furthermore, not all of the details from the passage are necessary to answer the questions. Therefore, it is a waste of your time to read and attempt to thoroughly understand the passage the first time you read it.

MAPPING A G-CHEM PASSAGE

As you skim through a G-Chem passage to get a feel for the type of questions that might follow, take note of the general location of information within the passage. The highlighting tool is a useful way to visually note a few key words that relate to the general topic of the passage or some unusual or new term that is introduced. Highlight sparingly, and use the scratch paper to make more detailed notes. An example of a highlighted passage is shown below. This is an Information Presentation passage:

The batteries that start an automobile or power flashlights are devices that convert chemical energy into electrical energy. These devices use spontaneous oxidation-reduction reactions (called half-reactions) that take place at the electrodes to create an electric current. The strength of the battery, or electromotive force, is determined by the difference in electric potential between the half cells, expressed in volts. This voltage depends on which reactions occur at the anode and the cathode, the concentrations of the solutions in the cells, and the temperature. The cell voltage, E, at a temperature of 25°C and nonstandard conditions, can be calculated from the Nernst equation, where $E°$ is the standard potential, n denotes the number of electrons transferred in the balanced half reaction, and Q is the reaction quotient.

$$E = E^{\circ} - \frac{0.0592}{n}\log_{10} Q$$

Equation 1

The lead storage battery used in automobiles is composed of six identical cells joined in series. The anode is solid lead, the cathode is lead dioxide, and the electrodes are immersed in a solution of sulfuric acid. As each cell discharges during normal operation, the sulfate ion is consumed as it is deposited in the form of lead sulfate on both electrodes, as shown in Reaction 1:

Reaction 1:

$$Pb(s) + PbO_2(s) + 4\ H^+(aq) + 2\ SO_4^{2-}(aq) \rightarrow 2\ PbSO_4(s) + 2\ H_2O(l)$$

Each cell produces 2 V, for a total of 12 V for the typical car battery. Unlike many batteries, however, the lead storage battery can be recharged by applying an external voltage. Because the redox reaction in the battery consumes sulfate ions, the degree of discharge of the battery can be checked by measuring the density of the battery fluid with a hydrometer. The fluid density in a fully charged battery is 1.2 g/cm^3.

Table 1 Standard Reduction Potentials at T = 25°C

Half-reaction	$E°$ (V)
$F_2(g) + 2e^- \rightarrow 2F^-(aq)$	+2.87
$Cl_2(g) + 2e^- \rightarrow 2Cl^-(aq)$	+1.36
$Cu^+(aq) + e^- \rightarrow Cu(s)$	+0.52
$Cu^{2+}(aq) + 2e^- \rightarrow Cu(s)$	+0.34
$Zn^{2+}(aq) + 2e^- \rightarrow Zn(s)$	–0.76
$Al^{3+}(aq) + 3e^- \rightarrow Al(s)$	–1.66
$Li^+(aq) + e^- \rightarrow Li(s)$	–3.05

Note that only a few words are highlighted. In the first paragraph, "batteries" and "spontaneous oxidation-reduction" relate to the general topic of the passage, and serve as a reminder that batteries contain a spontaneous redox reaction. The second paragraph identifies the two electrodes in the battery and, in the last paragraph, the voltage and density of a car battery are highlighted. Since these are specific and unusual pieces of information, they might come up in a question.

Rather than highlighting large portions of the passage as you skim it, use your scratch paper to create a simple passage map to help organize where different types of information are in the passage. Scratch paper is only useful if it is kept organized! Make sure that your notes for each passage are clearly delineated and marked with the passage number and range of questions on your scratch paper. This will allow you to easily read your notes when you come back to review a marked question. Resist the temptation to write in the first available blank space, as this makes it much more difficult to refer back to your work.

As you skim the passage, note the subject of each paragraph and any key words or values. A well-constructed passage map makes it easier and more efficient to go back and retrieve specific information as you work through the questions. Here is an example of a passage map for the passage shown above:

P1 – Batteries, general information, background
P2 – Automobile batteries, more specific information about them
P3 – Recharging car battery, Reduction Potentials in Table 1

As you can see, your passage map does not need to be particularly detailed, nor should it be, as reading and mapping the passage should only take a minute of your time. However, this does provide a valuable framework for efficiently locating information within the passage. You may find that highlighting the text in a General Chemistry passage is enough of a framework and reference for you, however, and many test-takers are just as successful without writing any information down on their scratch paper until they actually get into the specifics of the questions.

Let's look at another passage and how to map it. This is an Experiment/Research Presentation passage:

Two cube-shaped compartments, X and Y, each with a volume of one cubic meter, were used in several experiments to study the properties of gases. Compartment X was fitted with a piston of negligible mass which fit snugly against the walls of the container. The compartments were connected by a pinhole which could be opened or closed at will (see Figure 1). The pressure and temperature could be measured in either compartment. At the start of each experiment, Compartment X contained equal molar quantities of four gases (helium, oxygen, nitrogen, and carbon dioxide), the temperature in Compartment X was 25°C and the pressure was 1 atm. Initially, Compartment Y was evacuated. The behavior of all the gases can be assumed to be ideal. (Note: 1 atm ≈ 105 Pa.)

2.5

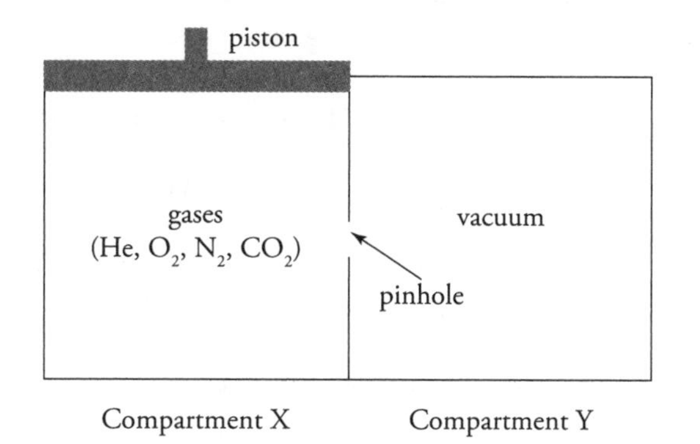

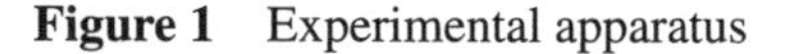

Figure 1 Experimental apparatus

Experiment 1:

With the pinhole closed, the temperature of the gases in Compartment X was gradually increased to 50°C, and the pressure of the gas inside the compartment was measured.

Experiment 2:

With the pinhole closed, the piston was gradually lowered into Compartment X until it had dropped a distance of 0.5 m. The pressure of the gas in the container was then measured.

Experiment 3:

The pinhole was opened, and the pressure change in each compartment was measured until equilibrium was reached.

Here, the highlighter tool can be used to emphasize that this passage is about the behavior of gases. Any time a passage is about gases, it's useful to know if the gas behaves in a real or ideal manner; therefore the phrase "assumed to be ideal" is also highlighted. In experimental passages, if important details jump out at you on your initial skim of the passage, it's useful to highlight them. For example, Figure 1 makes it fairly obvious that compartment X contains four gases, while compartment Y is a vacuum with no gas, however the "equal molar quantities" of the four gases in compartment X is a useful detail to highlight. Here's how you might map this passage on your scratch paper:

P1 – Experimental setup
E1 – Temp change, constant volume
E2 – Pressure change
E3 – Pressure change, equilibrium

As was true of our last passage map, the main purpose is to create an outline so that it will be easier to retrieve necessary information as you work through the questions. Since this is an Experiment Presentation passage, the map points out the location of the main experimental details. Note that on the first pass, it is not important to note all the specific details of each individual experiment on your scratch paper, though quickly highlighting new experimental conditions, like temperature, etc. can be helpful. If possible, however, it may be helpful to note the general variable being changed.

Let's look at one more example of passage mapping. This passage is a Persuasive Argument Passage:

Two theoretical chemists attempted to explain the observed trends of acidity by applying two interpretations of molecular orbital theory. Consider the pK_a values of some common acids listed along with the conjugate base of each acid:

acid	pK_a	conjugate base
H_2SO_4	< 0	HSO_4^-
H_2CrO_4	5.0	$HCrO_4^-$
H_3PO_4	2.1	$H_2PO_4^-$
HF	3.9	F^-
HOCl	7.8	ClO^-
HCN	9.5	CN^-
HIO_3	1.2	IO_3^-

Recall that acids with a $pK_a < 0$ are called strong acids, and those with a $pK_a > 0$ are called weak acids. The arguments of the chemists are given below.

Chemist #1:

"The acidity of a compound is proportional to the polarization of the H—X bond, where X is some nonmetal element. Complex acids, such as H_2SO_4, $HClO_4$, and HNO_3 are strong acids because the H—O bonding electrons are strongly drawn towards the oxygen. It is generally true that a covalent bond weakens as its polarization increases. Therefore, one can conclude that the strength of an acid is proportional to the number of electronegative atoms in that acid."

Chemist #2:

"The acidity of a compound is proportional to the number of stable resonance structures of that acid's conjugate base. H_2SO_4, $HClO_4$, and HNO_3 are all strong acids because their respective conjugate bases exhibit a high degree of resonance stabilization."

For a Persuasive Argument passage, the goal of passage mapping and highlighting is to identify the issue being addressed, and the main points of each of the opposing lines of reasoning. This can be accomplished using the highlighter tool to emphasize that the passage is about "trends of acidity", and that Chemist #1 attributes the behavior of acids to "polarization of the H—X bond," while Chemist #2 focuses on "number of stable resonance structures."

In this case, a passage map would be very similar to the results achieved by highlighting. However, keep in mind that the very act of writing things down helps clarify it in your head:

P1/Main issue: Trends of acidity, using MO theory
Chemist #1: acidity ∝ # of EN atoms; polarization of H—X bond
Chemist #2: # of res. struct. for conj. base

As you can see from the examples above, effective passage-mapping requires a combination of highlighting and jotting down notes in an organized fashion on your scratch paper. The best way to improve your passage mapping, and to determine which combination of these skills works best for you, is to practice, practice, practice.

2.6 TACKLING THE QUESTIONS

In general, G-Chem questions require a combination of basic knowledge, passage retrieval, and critical reasoning. The more difficult G-Chem questions tend to weigh the last two skills more heavily. Therefore, if you have a sound basis in the fundamental principles of General Chemistry, it is safe to assume that a tough question will be best addressed by looking back to the passage for information that is either explicitly stated or implied.

In the section on passage mapping, we reviewed an Information/Situation Presentation passage on batteries and redox reactions. We will draw on questions from this passage in order to illustrate the different question types.

G-Chem Memory Questions

These questions test background knowledge and require you to recall a specific definition or relationship. Memory questions are most often freestanding questions that appear on their own, without a passage associated with them. Memory questions are less frequently associated with passages on the MCAT, but when they are, they will help you complete a passage more quickly since there is no information retrieval required that will slow you down. For example, a question from the car battery passage shown above asked:

If the reaction in a concentration cell is spontaneous in the reverse direction, then:

A) $Q < K$, ΔG for the forward reaction is negative, and the cell voltage is positive.
B) $Q < K$, ΔG for the forward reaction is positive, and the cell voltage is negative.
C) $Q > K$, ΔG for the forward reaction is negative, and the cell voltage is positive.
D) $Q > K$, ΔG for the forward reaction is positive, and the cell voltage is negative.

In order to answer this question correctly, you need to know the connection between ΔG and spontaneity. A spontaneous reaction has a negative ΔG, and a nonspontaneous reaction has a positive ΔG. Since the reaction is spontaneous in the reverse direction, it must be nonspontaneous in the forward direction. Therefore, the ΔG of the forward reaction is positive, eliminating choices A and C. Alternatively, you could know that cell voltage applies to the forward direction, and that a nonspontaneous cell has a negative voltage, also eliminating choices A and C.

To distinguish between choices B and D, you must have a fundamental understanding of equilibrium and Le Châtelier's Principle. The reaction quotient, Q, always approaches the equilibrium constant, K, and if $Q > K$ the reaction will be pushed in the reverse direction, toward the reactants side of the equilibrium, in order to decrease the value of Q. Thus, since the question says the reaction is spontaneous in the reverse direction, Q must be greater than K. This makes choice D the best answer.

Also, note that this question asks about concentration cells, which are not mentioned in the passage, and therefore this problem is essentially a free-standing question.

G-Chem Explicit Questions

Explicit questions require direct retrieval of information from the passage. Sometimes, the answers to Explicit questions are definitions or relationships that are clearly stated in the passage. However, these types of questions may also require some background knowledge or a simple step of logical reasoning. Here is another example from the car battery redox passage shown above:

Of the following, which is the best reducing agent?

A) Li^+
B) Li
C) Cl^-
D) F^-

To answer this question, you must have fundamental knowledge of redox definitions and relationships, but you also need to retrieve information from the passage. The best reducing agent is the species that has the highest oxidizing potential, and Table 1 gives the reduction potentials for these reagents. However, you also need the knowledge that the oxidation potential is the same as the reduction potential, but with the opposite sign. Since the oxidation of Li has the highest positive potential (3.05 V), Li is the strongest reducing agent.

The best way to approach Explicit questions is to refer to your passage map to find the location of the information you need. Then, go back to the passage and read that section in greater detail. There are two instances when retrieval of information for Explicit questions can be especially tricky. First, in research study passages, be cautious when retrieving information from tables and graphs. Rather than simply pulling data directly from the figures, be sure to read the text just before and after the figures as well, as it may contain important information that changes the way the data should be interpreted. Second, when a passage goes into greater detail about a subject that you already have fundamental knowledge of, avoid the temptation to answer questions directly from memory. Often, these types of passages will provide some obscure detail or anomalous situation that will be tested in the questions, and require you to retrieve information from the passage in order to select the correct answer.

G-Chem Implicit Questions

Implicit questions require you to work through two or more steps of critical reasoning based on your background knowledge and information given in the passage. In other words, the answer is not directly stated in the passage, but is implied by the information provided. The distinction between an Implicit and an Explicit question can be subtle, as both require you to retrieve information from the passage, and Explicit questions may also require you to make a simple critical reasoning decision. The difference is that in Implicit questions, the reasoning step required is not as direct or obvious, and more than one step is usually required. For example:

When a lead storage battery recharges, what happens to the density of the battery fluid?

A) It decreases to 1.0 g/cm^3.
B) It increases to 1.0 g/cm^3.
C) It decreases to 1.2 g/cm^3.
D) It increases to 1.2 g/cm^3.

First, information on the density of the battery fluid must be retrieved from the passage. Our passage map tells us that specific information on car batteries can be found in paragraphs two and three, and reviewing the highlighted text reveals that in the third paragraph of the passage, it states that the density of fluid in a fully charged battery is 1.2 g/cm^3. Therefore, as the battery is recharging, its density is approaching this value, eliminating choices A and B.

The difference between choices C and D is whether the density of the solution is increasing or decreasing to 1.2 g/cm^3 during recharge. To determine this, we can look for additional information in the passage that may relate to changing density of the battery fluid. The second paragraph of the passage states that as the battery discharges, sulfate ions are consumed and deposited in the form of lead sulfate. The removal of ions from solution implies that the amount of mass in the solution is going down, and therefore its density is also decreasing. Therefore, density is decreasing during discharge, and increasing during recharge. This makes choice D the best answer.

The key step here is focusing on the differences among answer choices. What can be difficult about approaching implicit questions is that it is often hard to determine which information is supposed to "imply" something about the answer. Zeroing in on differences among the answer choices can help you determine which information from the passage is most relevant, and may help you rephrase what the question is really asking. Also, note that the first step of our analysis, eliminating the choices with 1.0 g/cm^3 density, was basically just answering an explicit question via direct passage retrieval. Many implicit questions begin this way, and it is much easier to eliminate answer choices first based on explicit information than it is to try to make a decision based on implicit information.

2.7 SUMMARY OF THE APPROACH TO GENERAL CHEMISTRY

How to Map the Passage and Use Scratch Paper

1) The passage should not be read like textbook material, with the intent of learning something from every sentence (science majors especially will be tempted to read this way). Skim through the paragraphs to get a feel for the type of questions that will follow, and to get a general idea of the location of information within the passage.
2) Highlighting—Use this tool sparingly, or you will end up with a passage that is completely covered in yellow highlighter! Highlighting in a General Chemistry passage should be used to draw attention to a few words that demonstrate one of the following:
    - The main theme of a paragraph
    - Important predictions or conclusions about an experiment
    - Any unusual or unfamiliar terms that are defined specifically for that passage (like something that is italicized)
3) Pay brief attention to equations, figures, and experiments, noting only what information they deal with (i.e., read titles, axes, and column/row headings). Do not spend a lot of time analyzing at this point, as you can come back and look more closely at this information if a question requires it.
4) Scratch paper is only useful if it is kept organized! Make sure that your notes for each passage are clearly delineated and marked with the passage number and range of questions on your scratch paper. This will allow you to easily read your notes when you come back to review a marked question. Resist the temptation to write in the first available blank space, as this makes it much more difficult to refer back to your work.

General Chemistry Question Strategies

1) Remember that Process of Elimination is paramount! The strikeout tool allows you to eliminate answer choices; this will improve your chances of guessing the correct answer if you are unable to narrow it down to one choice.
2) Answer the straightforward questions first. Leave questions that require analysis of experiments and graphs for later. Take the test in the order YOU want. Make sure to use your scratch paper to indicate questions you skipped.
3) Make sure that the answer you choose actually answers the question, and isn't just a true statement.
4) I-II-III questions: Always work between the I-II-III statements and the answer choices. Unfortunately, it is not possible to strike out the Roman numerals, but this is a great use for scratch paper notes. Once a statement is determined to be true (or false), strike out answer choices that do not contain (or do contain) that statement.
5) LEAST/EXCEPT/NOT questions: Don't get tricked by these questions that ask you to pick the answer that doesn't fit (the incorrect or false statement). It's often good to use your scratch paper and write a T or F next to answer choices A–D. The one that stands out as different is the correct answer. Don't forget that you can also highlight information in the question stem, so draw attention to the LEAST/EXCEPT/NOT in the question so you don't forget!
6) 2 x 2 style questions: These questions require you to know two pieces of information to get the correct answer, and are easily identified by their answer choices, which commonly take the form A because X, B because X, A because Y, B because Y. Tackle one piece of information at a time, which should allow you to quickly eliminate two answer choices.
7) Ranking questions: When asked to rank items, look for an extreme—either the greatest or the smallest item—and eliminate answer choices that do not have that item shown at the correct end of the ranking. This is often enough to eliminate one to three answer choices. Based on the remaining choices, look for the other extreme at the other end of the ranking and use POE again.
8) If you read a question and do not know how to answer it, look to the passage for help. It is likely that the passage contains information pertinent to answering the question, either within the text or in the form of experimental data.
9) If a question requires a lengthy calculation, mark it and return to it later, particularly if you are slow with arithmetic or dimensional analysis.
10) Again, don't leave any question blank, and when randomly guessing, choose the same letter for every question unless you have already eliminated it.

A Note About Flashcards

For most of the exams you've taken previously, flashcards were likely very helpful. This was because those exams mostly required you to regurgitate information, and flashcards are pretty good at helping you memorize facts. However, the most challenging aspect of the MCAT is not that it requires you to memorize the fine details of content knowledge, but that it requires you to apply your basic scientific knowledge to unfamiliar situations: flashcards alone may not help you there.

Flashcards can be beneficial if your basic content knowledge is deficient in some area. For example, if you don't know the strong acids and bases, flashcards can certainly help you memorize these facts. Or, maybe you are unsure of some of the molecular geometries and shapes from the VSEPR theory. You might find that flashcards can help you memorize these. But unless you are trying to memorize basic facts in your personal weak areas, you are better off doing and analyzing practice passages than carrying around a stack of flashcards.

Chapter 3
Chemistry Fundamentals

3.1 METRIC UNITS

Before we begin our study of chemistry, we will briefly go over metric units. Scientists use the *Système International d'Unitès* (the International System of Units), abbreviated SI, to express measurements of physical quantities. The six MCAT-relevant **base units** of SI are given below:

SI Base Unit	Abbreviation	Measures
meter	m	length
kilogram	kg	mass
second	s	time
mole	mol	amount of substance
kelvin	K	temperature
ampere	A	electric current

The units of any physical quantity can be written in terms of the SI base units. For example, the SI unit of speed is meters per second (m/s), the SI unit of energy (the joule) is kilograms times meters^2 per second^2 ($kg \cdot m^2/s^2$), and so forth.

Multiples of the base units that are powers of ten are often abbreviated and precede the symbol for the unit. For example, m is the symbol for milli-, which means 10^{-3} (one thousandth). So, one thousandth of a second, 1 millisecond, would be written as 1 ms. The letter M is the symbol for mega-, which means 10^6 (one million); a distance of one million meters, 1 megameter, would be abbreviated as 1 Mm. Some of the most common power-of-ten prefixes are given in the list below:

Prefix	Symbol	Multiple
nano-	n	10^{-9}
micro-	μ	10^{-6}
milli-	m	10^{-3}
centi-	c	10^{-2}
kilo-	k	10^{3}
mega-	M	10^{6}

Two other units, ones that are common in chemistry, are the liter and the angstrom. The liter (abbreviated L) is a unit of volume equal to 1/1000 of a cubic meter:

$$1000 \text{ L} = 1 \text{ m}^3$$

$$1 \text{ L} = 1000 \text{ cm}^3$$

The standard SI unit of volume, the cubic meter, is inconveniently large for most laboratory work. The liter is a smaller unit. Furthermore, the most common way of expressing solution concentrations, **molarity** (*M*), uses the liter in its definition: M = moles of solute per liter of solution.

In addition, you will see the milliliter (mL) as often as you will see the liter. A simple consequence of the definition of a liter is the fact that one milliliter is the same volume as one cubic centimeter:

$$1 \text{ mL} = 1 \text{ cm}^3 = 1 \text{ cc}$$

While the volume of any substance can, strictly speaking, be expressed in liters, you rarely hear of a milliliter of gold, for example. Ordinarily, the liter is used to express the volumes of liquids and gases, but not solids.

The **angstrom**, abbreviated Å, is a unit of length equal to 10^{-10} m. The angstrom is convenient because atomic radii and bond lengths are typically around 1 to 3 Å.

Example 3-1: By how many orders of magnitude is a centimeter longer than an angstrom?

Solution: An **order of magnitude** is a factor of ten. Since 1 cm = 10^{-2} m and 1 Å = 10^{-10} m, a centimeter is 8 factors of ten, or 8 orders of magnitude, greater than an angstrom.

3.2 DENSITY

The **density** of a substance is its mass per volume:

$$\text{Density: } \rho = \frac{\text{mass}}{\text{volume}} = \frac{m}{V} \quad \frac{\text{g}}{\text{cm}^3}$$

In SI units, density is expressed in kilograms per cubic meter (kg/m^3). However, in chemistry, densities are more often expressed in grams per cubic centimeter (g/cm^3). This unit of density is convenient because most liquids and solids have a density of around 1 to 20 g/cm^3. Here is the conversion between these two sets of density units:

$$\text{g/cm}^3 \rightarrow \text{multiply by 1000} \rightarrow \text{kg/m}^3$$

$$\text{g/cm}^3 \leftarrow \text{divide by 1000} \leftarrow \text{kg/m}^3$$

For example, water has a density of 1 g/cm^3 (it varies slightly with temperature, but this is the value the MCAT will expect you to use). To write this density in kg/m^3, we would multiply by 1000. The density of water is 1000 kg/m^3. As another example, the density of copper is about 9000 kg/m^3, so to express this density in g/cm^3, we would divide by 1000: The density of copper is 9 g/cm^3.

Example 3-2: Diamond has a density of 3500 kg/m^3. What is the volume, in cm^3, of a 1 3/4-carat diamond (where, by definition, 1 carat = 0.2 g)?

Solution: If we divide mass by density, we get volume, so, converting 3500 kg/m^3 into 3.5 g/cm^3, we find that

$$V = \frac{m}{\rho} = \frac{1.75(0.2\text{ g})}{3.5\text{ g/cm}^3} = \frac{0.35\text{ g}}{3.5\text{ g/cm}^3} = 0.1\text{ cm}^3$$

3.3 MOLECULAR FORMULAS

When two or more atoms form a covalent bond they create a **molecule**. For example, when two atoms of hydrogen (H) bond with one atom of oxygen (O), the resulting molecule is H_2O, water. A compound's **molecular formula** gives the identities and numbers of the atoms in the molecule. For example, the formula $C_4H_4N_2$ tells us that this molecule contains four carbon atoms, four hydrogen atoms, and two nitrogen atoms.

Example 3-3: What is the molecular formula of *para*-nitrotoluene?

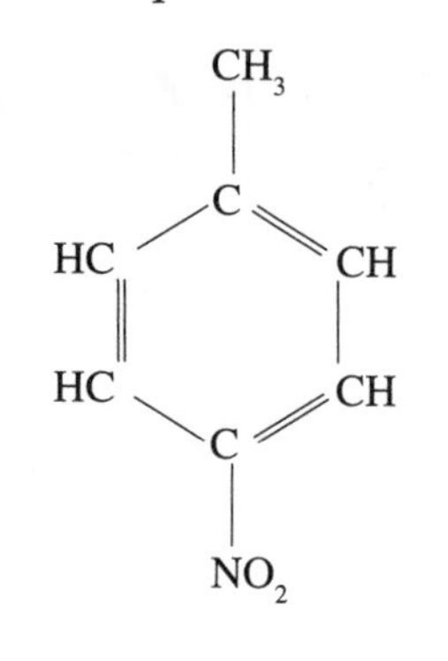

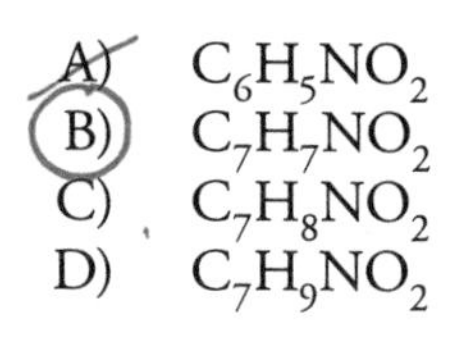

Solution: There are a total of seven carbon atoms, seven hydrogen atoms, one nitrogen atom, and two oxygen atoms, so choice B is the correct answer.

3.4 EMPIRICAL FORMULAS

Let's look again at the molecule $C_4H_4N_2$. There are four atoms each of carbon and hydrogen, and half as many (two) nitrogen atoms. Therefore, the smallest whole numbers that give the same *ratio* of atoms (carbon to hydrogen to nitrogen) in this molecule are 2:2:1. If we use *these* numbers for the atoms, we get the molecule's **empirical formula**: C_2H_2N. In general, to reduce a molecular formula to the empirical formula, divide all the subscripts by their greatest common factor. Here are a few more examples:

Molecular Formula	Empirical Formula
$C_6H_{12}O_6$	CH_2O
$K_2S_2O_8$	KSO_4
$Fe_4Na_8O_{35}P_{10}$	$Fe_4Na_8O_{35}P_{10}$
$C_{30}H_{27}N_3O_{15}$	$C_{10}H_9NO_5$

Example 3-4: What is the empirical formula for ethylene glycol, $C_2H_6O_2$?

A) CH_3O
B) CH_4O
C) CH_6O
D) $C_2H_6O_2$

Solution: Dividing each of the subscripts of $C_2H_6O_2$ by 2, we get CH_3O, choice A.

3.5 POLYATOMIC IONS

You should also be familiar with a handful of common polyatomic ions for the MCAT. Those in the table below are the ones you're most likely to come across.

Name	Formula
Ammonium	NH_4^+
Hydronium	H_3O^+
Acetate (AcO⁻)	$CH_3CO_2^-$
Bicarbonate	HCO_3^-
Cyanide	CN^-
Hydroxide	OH^-
Nitrate	NO_3^-
Nitrite	NO_2^-
Perchlorate	ClO_4^-
Carbonate	CO_3^{2-}
Sulfate	SO_4^{2-}
Sulfite	SO_3^{2-}
Phosphate	PO_4^{3-}

3.6 FORMULA AND MOLECULAR WEIGHT

If we know the chemical formula, we can figure out the **formula weight**, which is the sum of the atomic weights of all the atoms in the molecule. The unit for atomic weight is the **atomic mass unit**, abbreviated **amu**. (Note: Although *weight* is the popular term, it should really be *mass*.) One atomic mass unit is, by definition, equal to exactly 1/12 the mass of an atom of carbon-12 (^{12}C), the most abundant naturally occurring form of carbon. The periodic table lists the atomic mass of each element, which is actually a weighted average of the atomic masses of all its naturally occurring forms (isotopes) based on their relative abundance. To calculate the formula weight of the compound in question, refer to the periodic table. The atomic mass of carbon is 12.0 amu, that of hydrogen is 1.0 amu, and that of nitrogen as 14.0 amu. Therefore, the formula weight for $C_4H_4N_2$ is

$$4(12) + 4(1) + 2(14) = 80$$

(The unit *amu* may not be explicitly included.) When a compound exists as discrete molecules, the term **molecular weight** (MW) is usually used instead of formula weight. For example, the molecular weight of water, H_2O, is 2(1) + 16 = 18. The term formula weight is usually used for *ionic* compounds, such as NaCl. The formula weight of NaCl is 23 + 35.5 = 58.5.

Example 3-5: What is the formula weight of calcium phosphate, $Ca_3(PO_4)_2$?

A) 310 amu
B) 350 amu
C) 405 amu
D) 450 amu

Solution: The masses of the elements are Ca = 40 amu, P = 31 amu, and O = 16 amu. Therefore, the formula weight of calcium phosphate is

$$3(40\text{ amu}) + 2(31\text{ amu}) + 8(16\text{ amu}) = 310\text{ amu}$$

Choice A is the answer.

3.7 THE MOLE

A **mole** is simply a particular number of things, like a dozen is any group of 12 things. One mole of anything contains 6.02×10^{23} entities. A mole of atoms is a collection of 6.02×10^{23} atoms; a mole of molecules contains 6.02×10^{23} molecules, and so on. This number, 6.02×10^{23}, is called **Avogadro's number,** denoted by N_A (or N_0). What is so special about 6.02×10^{23}? The answer is based on the atomic mass unit, which is defined so that the mass of a carbon-12 atom is exactly 12 amu. *The number of carbon-12 atoms in a sample of mass of 12 grams is* 6.02×10^{23}. Avogadro's number is the link between atomic mass units and grams. For example, the periodic table lists the mass of sodium (Na, atomic number 11) as 23.0. This means that 1 atom of sodium has a mass of 23 atomic mass units, or that 1 *mole* of sodium atoms has a mass of 23 *grams.*

Since 1 mole of a substance has a mass in grams equal to the mass in amus of 1 formula unit of the substance, we have the following formula:

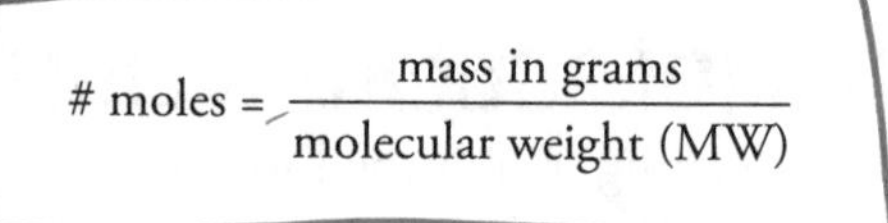

$$\#\text{ moles} = \frac{\text{mass in grams}}{\text{molecular weight (MW)}}$$

Example 3-6:

a) Which has the greater formula weight: potassium dichromate ($K_2Cr_2O_7$) or lead azide $Pb(N_3)_2$?
b) Which contains more formula units: a 1-mole sample of potassium dichromate or a 1-mole sample of lead azide?

Solution:

a) The formula weight of potassium dichromate is

$$2(39.1) + 2(52) + 7(16) = 294.2$$

and the formula weight of lead azide is

$$207.2 + 6(14) = 291.2$$

Therefore, potassium dichromate has the greater formula weight.

b) Trick question. Both samples contain the same number of formula units, namely 1 mole of them. (Which weighs more: a pound of rocks or a pound of feathers?)

Example 3-7: How many molecules of hydrazine, N_2H_4, are in a sample with a mass of 96 grams?

Solution: The molecular weight of N_2H_4 is 2(14) + 4(1) = 32. This means that 1 mole of N_2H_4 has a mass of 32 grams. Therefore, a sample that has a mass of 96 grams contains 3 moles of molecules, because the formula above tells us that

$$n = \frac{96 \text{ g}}{32 \text{ g/mol}} = 3 \text{ moles}$$

3.8 PERCENTAGE COMPOSITION BY MASS

A molecule's molecular or empirical formula can be used to determine the molecule's percent mass composition. For example, let's find the mass composition of carbon, hydrogen, and nitrogen in $C_4H_4N_2$. Using the compound's empirical formula, C_2H_2N, will give us the same answer but the calculations will be easier because we'll have smaller numbers to work with. The empirical molecular weight is 2(12) + 2(1) + 14 = 40, so each element's contribution to the total mass is

$$\%C = \frac{2(12)}{40} = \frac{12}{20} = \frac{60}{100} = 60\%, \quad \%H = \frac{2(1)}{40} = \frac{1}{20} = \frac{5}{100} = 5\%, \quad \%N = \frac{14}{40} = \frac{7}{20} = \frac{35}{100} = 35\%$$

We can also use information about the percentage composition to determine a compound's empirical formula. Suppose a substance is analyzed and found to consist, by mass, of 70 percent iron and 30 percent oxygen. To find the empirical formula for this compound, the trick is to start with 100 grams of the substance. We choose 100 grams since percentages are based on parts in 100. One hundred grams of this substance would then contain 70 g of Fe and 30 g of O. Now, how many *moles* of Fe and O are present in this 100-gram substance? Since the atomic weight of Fe is 55.8 and that of O is 16, we can use the formula given above in Section 3.6 and find

$$\text{\# moles of Fe} = \frac{70 \text{ g}}{55.8 \text{ g/mol}} \approx \frac{70}{56} = \frac{5}{4} \quad \text{and} \quad \text{\# moles of O} = \frac{30 \text{ g}}{16 \text{ g/mol}} = \frac{15}{8}$$

Because the empirical formula involves the ratio of the numbers of atoms, let's find the ratio of the amount of Fe to the amount of O:

$$\text{Ratio of Fe to O} = \frac{5/4 \text{ mol}}{15/8 \text{ mol}} = \frac{5}{4} \cdot \frac{8}{15} = \frac{2}{3}$$

Since the ratio of Fe to O is 2:3, the empirical formula of the substance is Fe_2O_3.

Example 3-8: What is the percent composition by mass of each element in sodium azide, NaN_3?

A) Sodium 25%; nitrogen 75%
B) Sodium 35%; nitrogen 65%
C) Sodium 55%; nitrogen 45%
D) Sodium 65%; nitrogen 35%

Solution: The molecular weight of this compound is 23 + 3(14) = 65. Therefore, sodium's contribution to the total mass is

$$\%\text{Na} = \frac{23}{65} \approx \frac{1}{3} \approx 33\%$$

Without even calculating nitrogen's contribution, we already see that choice B is best.

Example 3-9: What is the percent composition by mass of carbon in glucose, $C_6H_{12}O_6$?

A) 40%
B) 50%
C) 67%
D) 75%

Solution: The empirical formula for this compound is CH_2O, so the empirical molecular weight is 12 + 2(1) + 16 = 30. Therefore, carbon's contribution to the total mass is

$$\%\text{C} = \frac{12}{30} = 40\%$$

So choice A is the answer. We would have found the same answer using the molecular formula, but the numbers would have been messier:

$$\%\text{C} = \frac{6(12)}{6(12) + 12(1) + 6(16)} = \frac{72}{180} = 40\%$$

Example 3-10: What is the empirical formula of a compound that is, by mass, 90 percent carbon and 10 percent hydrogen?

A) CH_2
B) C_2H_3
C) C_3H_4
D) C_4H_5

Solution: A 100-gram sample of this compound would contain 90 g of C and 10 g of H. Since the atomic weight of C is 12 and that of H is 1, we have

$$\text{\# moles of C} = \frac{90 \text{ g}}{12 \text{ g/mol}} = \frac{15}{2} \quad \text{and} \quad \text{\# moles of H} = \frac{10 \text{ g}}{1 \text{ g/mol}} = 10$$

Therefore, the ratio of the amount of C to the amount of H is

$$\frac{15/2 \text{ mol}}{10 \text{ mol}} = \frac{3}{4}$$

Because the ratio of C to H is 3:4, the empirical formula of the compound is C_3H_4, and choice C is the answer.

Example 3-11: What is the percent by mass of water in the hydrate $MgCl_2 \cdot 5H_2O$?

A) 27%
B) 36%
C) 49%
D) 52%

Solution: The formula weight for this hydrate is 24.3 + 2(35.5) + 5[2(1) + 16] = 185.3. Since water's total molecular weight in this compound is 5[2(1) + 16] = 90, we see that water's contribution to the total mass is $\%H_2O = 90/185.3$, which is a little *less* than one half (50 percent). Therefore, the answer is C.

Example 3-12: In which of the following compounds is the mass percent of each of the constituent elements nearly identical?

A) NaCl
B) LiBr
C) HCl
D) CaF_2

Solution: The question is asking us to identify the compound made up of equal amounts, by mass, of two elements. Looking at the given compounds, we see that

$$\text{Na (23.0 g/mol)} \neq \text{Cl (35.5 g/mol)}$$

$$\text{Li (6.9 g/mol)} \neq \text{Br (79.9 g/mol)}$$

$$\text{H (1.0 g/mol)} \neq \text{Cl (35.5 g/mol)}$$

$$\text{Ca (40.1 g/mol)} \approx \text{2 F } (2\times19) = \text{38 g/mol)}$$

Therefore, choice D is best.

3.9 CONCENTRATION

Molarity (*M*) expresses the concentration of a solution in terms of moles of solute per volume (in liters) of solution:

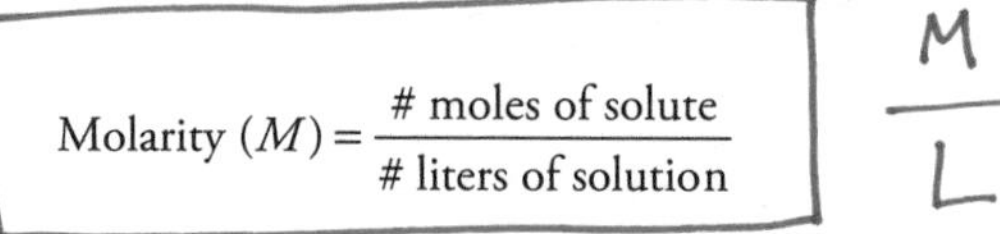

$$\text{Molarity } (M) = \frac{\text{\# moles of solute}}{\text{\# liters of solution}}$$

Concentration is denoted by enclosing the solute in brackets. For instance, "$[Na^+] = 1.0\ M$" indicates a solution in which the concentration is equivalent to 1 mole of sodium ions per liter of solution.

Mole fraction simply expresses the fraction of moles of a given substance (which we'll denote here by S) relative to the total moles in a solution:

$$\text{mole fraction of S} = X_S = \frac{\text{\# moles of substance S}}{\text{total \# moles in solution}}$$

Mole fraction is a useful way to express concentration when more than one solute is present, and is often used when discussing the composition of a mixture of gases.

3.10 CHEMICAL EQUATIONS AND STOICHIOMETRIC COEFFICIENTS

The equation

$$2\ Al + 6\ HCl \rightarrow 2\ AlCl_3 + 3\ H_2$$

describes the reaction of aluminum metal (Al) with hydrochloric acid (HCl) to produce aluminum chloride ($AlCl_3$) and hydrogen gas (H_2). The **reactants** are on the left side of the arrow, and the **products** are on the right side. A chemical equation is **balanced** if, for every element represented, the number of atoms on the left side of the arrow is equal to the number of atoms on the right side. This illustrates the **Law of Conservation of Mass** (or of **Matter**), which says that the amount of matter (and thus mass) does not change in a chemical reaction. For a *balanced* reaction such as the one above, the coefficients (2, 6, 2, and 3) preceding each compound—which are known as **stoichiometric coefficients**—tell us in what proportion the reactants react and in what proportion the products are formed. For this reaction, 2 atoms of Al react with 6 molecules of HCl to form 2 formula units of $AlCl_3$ and 3 molecules of H_2. The equation also means that 2 *moles* of Al react with 6 *moles* of HCl to form 2 *moles* of $AlCl_3$ and 3 *moles* of H_2.

The stoichiometric coefficients give the ratios of the number of molecules (or moles) that apply to the combination of reactants and the formation of products. They do *not* give the ratios by mass.

Balancing Equations

Balancing most chemical equations is simply a matter of trial and error. It's a good idea to start with the most complex species in the reaction. For example, let's look at the reaction above:

$$Al + HCl \rightarrow AlCl_3 + H_2 \text{ (unbalanced)}$$

Start with the most complex molecule, $AlCl_3$. The total number of atoms, or moles of atoms, is calculated by multiplying the coefficient in front of a compound times the subscript within the formula. To get 3 atoms of Cl on the product side, we need to have 3 atoms of Cl on the reactant side; therefore, we put a 3 in front of the HCl:

$$Al + 3\ HCl \rightarrow AlCl_3 + H_2 \text{ (unbalanced)}$$

We've now balanced the Cl's, but the H's are still unbalanced. Since we have 3 H's on the left, we need 3 H's on the right to accomplish this, so we put a coefficient of 3/2 in front of the H_2:

$$Al + 3\ HCl \rightarrow AlCl_3 + 3/2\ H_2$$

Notice that we put a 3/2 (*not* a 3) in front of the H_2, because a hydrogen molecule contains 2 hydrogen atoms. All the atoms are now balanced—we see 1 Al, 3 H's, and 3 Cl's on each side. Because it's customary to write stoichiometric coefficients as whole numbers, we simply multiply through by 2 to get rid of the fraction and write

$$2\ Al + 6\ HCl \rightarrow 2\ AlCl_3 + 3\ H_2$$

Example 3-13: Balance each of these equations:

a) $NH_3 + O_2 \rightarrow NO + H_2O$
b) $CuCl_2 + NH_3 + H_2O \rightarrow Cu(OH)_2 + NH_4Cl$
c) $C_3H_8 + O_2 \rightarrow CO_2 + H_2O$
d) $C_8H_{18} + O_2 \rightarrow CO_2 + H_2O$

Solution:

a) $4\ NH_3 + 5\ O_2 \rightarrow 4\ NO + 6\ H_2O$
b) $CuCl_2 + 2\ NH_3 + 2\ H_2O \rightarrow Cu(OH)_2 + 2\ NH_4Cl$
c) $C_3H_8 + 5\ O_2 \rightarrow 3\ CO_2 + 4\ H_2O$
d) $2\ C_8H_{18} + 25\ O_2 \rightarrow 16\ CO_2 + 18\ H_2O$

3.11 STOICHIOMETRIC RELATIONSHIPS IN BALANCED REACTIONS

Once the equation for a chemical reaction is balanced, the stoichiometric coefficients tell us the relative amounts of the reactant species that combine and the relative amounts of the product species that are formed. For example, recall that the reaction

$$2\ Al + 6\ HCl \rightarrow 2\ AlCl_3 + 3\ H_2$$

tells us that 2 moles of Al react with 6 moles of HCl to form 2 moles of $AlCl_3$ and 3 moles of H_2.

Example 3-14: If 108 grams of aluminum metal are consumed, how many grams of hydrogen gas will be produced?

Solution: Because the stoichiometric coefficients give the ratios of the number of moles that apply to the combination of reactants and the formation of products—not the ratios by mass—we first need to determine how many *moles* of Al react. Since the molecular weight of Al is 27, we know that 27 grams of Al is equivalent to 1 mole. Therefore, 108 grams of Al is 4 moles. Now we use the stoichiometry of the balanced equation: for every 2 moles of Al that react, 3 moles of H_2 are produced. So, if 4 moles of Al react, we'll get 6 moles of H_2. Finally, we convert the number of moles of H_2 produced to grams. The molecular weight of H_2 is 2(1) = 2. This means that 1 mole of H_2 has a mass of 2 grams. Therefore, 6 moles of H_2 will have a mass of 6(2 g) = 12 grams.

Example 3-15: How many grams of HCl are required to produce 534 grams of aluminum chloride?

Solution: First, we'll convert the desired mass of $AlCl_3$ into moles. The molecular weight of $AlCl_3$ is 27 + 3(35.5) = 133.5. This means that 1 mole of $AlCl_3$ has a mass of 133.5 grams. Therefore, 534 grams of $AlCl_3$ is equivalent to 534/133.5 = 4 moles. Next, we use the stoichiometry of the balanced equation. For every 2 moles of $AlCl_3$ that are produced, 6 moles of HCl are consumed. So, if we want to produce 4 moles of $AlCl_3$, we'll need 12 moles of HCl. Finally, we convert the number of moles of HCl consumed to grams. The molecular weight of HCl is 1 + 35.5 = 36.5. This means that 1 mole of HCl has a mass of 36.5 grams. Therefore, 12 moles of HCl will have a mass of 12(36.5 g) = 438 grams.

Example 3-16: Consider the following reaction:

$$CS_2 + 3\ O_2 \rightarrow CO_2 + 2\ SO_2$$

How much carbon disulfide must be used to produce 64 grams of SO_2?

A) 38 g
B) 57 g
C) 76 g
D) 114 g

Solution: Since the molecular weight of SO_2 is 32.1 + 2(16) = 64, we know that 64 grams of SO_2 is equivalent to 1 mole. From the stoichiometry of the balanced equation, we see that for every 1 mole of CS_2 that reacts, 2 moles of SO_2 are produced. Therefore, to produce just 1 mole of SO_2, we need 1/2 mole of CS_2. The molecular weight of CS_2 is 12 + 2(32.1) ≈ 76, so 1/2 mole of CS_2 has a mass of 38 grams. The answer is A.

3.12 THE LIMITING REAGENT

Let's look again at the reaction of aluminum with hydrochloric acid:

$$2\ Al + 6\ HCl \rightarrow 2\ AlCl_3 + 3\ H_2$$

Suppose that this reaction starts with 4 moles of Al and 18 moles of HCl. We have enough HCl to make 6 moles of $AlCl_3$ and 9 moles of H_2. *However,* there's only enough Al to make 4 moles of $AlCl_3$ and 6 moles of H_2. There isn't enough aluminum metal (Al) to make use of all the available HCl. As the reaction proceeds, we'll run out of aluminum. This means that aluminum is the **limiting reagent** here, because we run out of this reactant *first,* so it limits how much product the reaction can produce.

Now suppose that the reaction begins with 4 moles of Al and 9 moles of HCl. There's enough Al metal to produce 4 moles of $AlCl_3$ and 6 moles of H_2. But there's only enough HCl to make 3 moles of $AlCl_3$ and 4.5 moles of H_2. There isn't enough HCl to make use of all the available aluminum metal. As the reaction proceeds, we'll find that all the HCl is consumed before the Al is consumed. In this situation, HCl is the limiting reagent. Notice that we had more moles of HCl than we had of Al and the initial mass of the HCl was greater than the initial mass of Al. Nevertheless, the limiting reagent in this case was the HCl. The limiting reagent is the reactant that is consumed first, not necessarily the reactant that's initially present in the smallest amount.

Example 3-17: Consider the following reaction:

$$2\ ZnS + 3\ O_2 \rightarrow 2\ ZnO + 2\ SO_2$$

If 97.5 grams of zinc sulfide undergoes this reaction with 32 grams of oxygen gas, what will be the limiting reagent?

A) ZnS
B) O_2
C) ZnO
D) SO_2

Solution: Since the molecular weight of ZnS is 65.4 + 32.1 = 97.5 and the molecular weight of O_2 is 2(16) = 32, this reaction begins with 1 mole of ZnS and 1 mole of O_2. From the stoichiometry of the balanced equation, we see that 1 mole of ZnS would react completely with $\frac{3}{2}$ = 1.5 moles of O_2. Because we have only 1 mole of O_2, the O_2 will be consumed first; it is the limiting reagent, and the answer is B. Note that choice C and D can be eliminated immediately, because a limiting reagent is always a reactant.

3.13 SOME NOTATION USED IN CHEMICAL EQUATIONS

In addition to specifying what atoms or molecules are involved in a chemical reaction, an equation may contain additional information. One type of additional information that can be written right into the equation specifies the **phases** of the substances in the reaction, i.e., if the substance is a solid, liquid, or gas. Another common condition is that a substance may be dissolved in water when the reaction proceeds. In this case, we'd say the substance is in aqueous solution. These four "states" are abbreviated and written in parentheses as follows:

Solid	(*s*)
Liquid	(*l*)
Gas	(*g*)
Aqueous	(*aq*)

These immediately follow the chemical symbol for the reactant or product in the equation. For example, the reaction of sodium metal with water, which produces sodium hydroxide and hydrogen gas, could be written like this:

$$2\ Na(s) + 2\ H_2O(l) \rightarrow 2\ NaOH(aq) + H_2(g)$$

In some cases, the reactants are heated to produce the desired reaction. To indicate this, we write a "Δ"—or the word "heat"—above (or below) the reaction arrow. For example, heating potassium nitrate produces potassium nitrite and oxygen gas:

$$2\ KNO_3(s) \xrightarrow{\Delta} 2\ KNO_2(aq) + O_2(g)$$

Some reactions proceed more rapidly in the presence of a **catalyst**, which is a substance that increases the rate of a reaction without being consumed. For example, in the industrial production of sulfuric acid, an intermediate step is the reaction of sulfur dioxide and oxygen to produce sulfur trioxide. Not only are the reactants heated, but they are combined in the presence of V_2O_5. We indicate the presence of a catalyst by writing it below the arrow in the equation:

$$2\ SO_2 + O_2 \xrightarrow[V_2O_5]{\Delta} 2\ SO_3$$

3.14 OXIDATION STATES

An atom's **oxidation state** (or **oxidation number**) is meant to indicate how the atom's "ownership" of its valence electrons changes when it forms a compound. For example, consider the formula unit NaCl. The sodium atom will transfer its valence electron to the chlorine atom, so the sodium's "ownership" of its valence electron has certainly changed. To indicate this, we'd say that the oxidation state of sodium is now +1 (or 1 *less* electron than it started with). On the other hand, chlorine accepts ownership of that 1 electron, so its oxidation state is –1 (that is, 1 *more* electron than it started with). Giving up ownership results in a more positive oxidation state; accepting ownership results in a more negative oxidation state.

This example of NaCl is rather special (and easy) since the compound is **ionic**, and we consider ionic compounds to involve the complete transfer of electrons. But what about a non-ionic (that is, a **covalent**) compound? *The oxidation state of an atom is the "charge" it would have if the compound were ionic.* Here's another way of saying this: the oxidation state of an atom in a molecule is the charge it would have if all the shared electrons were completely transferred to the more electronegative element. Note that for covalent compounds, this is not a real charge, just a bookkeeping trick.

The following list gives the rules for assigning oxidation states to the atoms in a molecule. If following one rule in the list causes the violation of another rule, the rule that is higher in the list takes precedence.

Rules for Assigning Oxidation States

1) The oxidation state of any element in its standard state is 0.
2) The sum of the oxidation states of the atoms in a neutral molecule must always be 0, and the sum of the oxidation states of the atoms in an ion must always equal the ion's charge.
3) Group 1 metals have a +1 oxidation state, and Group 2 metals have a +2 oxidation state.
4) Fluorine has a –1 oxidation state.
5) Hydrogen has a +1 oxidation state when bonded to something more electronegative than carbon, a –1 oxidation state when bonded to an atom less electronegative than carbon, and a 0 oxidation state when bonded to carbon.
6) Oxygen has a –2 oxidation state.
7) The rest of the halogens have a –1 oxidation state, and the atoms of the oxygen family have a –2 oxidation state.

It's worth noting a common exception to Rule 6: In peroxides (such as H_2O_2 or Na_2O_2), oxygen is in a –1 oxidation state (which is consistent with Rules 3 and 5 having a higher priority than rule 6).

As we will discuss later, the order of electronegativities of some elements can be remembered with the mnemonic FONClBrISCH (pronounced "fawn-cull-brish"). This lists the elements in order from the most electronegative (F) to the least electronegative (H). Hence, bonds from H to anything before C in FONClBrISCH will give hydrogen a +1 oxidation state, and bonds from H to anything *not* found in the list will give H a –1 oxidation state.

Let's find the oxidation number of manganese in $KMnO_4$. By Rule 3, K is +1, and by Rule 6, O is –2. Therefore, the oxidation state of Mn must be +7 in order for the sum of all the oxidation numbers in this electrically-neutral molecule to be zero (the unbreakable Rule 2).

Like many other elements, transition metals can assume different oxidation states, depending on the compound they're in. (Note, however, that a metal will never assume a negative oxidation state!) For example, iron has an oxidation number of +2 in $FeCl_2$ but an oxidation number of +3 in $FeCl_3$. The oxidation number of a transition metal is given as a Roman numeral in the name of the compound. Therefore, $FeCl_2$ is iron(II) chloride, and $FeCl_3$ is iron(III) chloride.

Example 3-18: Determine the oxidation state of the atoms in each of the following molecules:

a) NO_3^-
b) HNO_2
c) O_2
d) SF_4

Solution:

a) By Rule 6, the oxidation state of O is –2; therefore, by Rule 2, the oxidation state of N must be +5.
b) By Rule 5, the oxidation state of H is +1, and by Rule 6, O has an oxidation state of –2. Therefore, by Rule 2, N must have an oxidation state of +3 in this molecule.
c) By Rule 1 (which is higher in the list than Rule 5 and thus takes precedence), each O atom in O_2 has an oxidation state of 0.
d) By Rule 4, F has an oxidation state of –1. So, by Rule 2, S has an oxidation state of +4.

Chapter 4
Atomic Structure and Periodic Trends

1 H 1.0																	2 He 4.0
3 Li 6.9	4 Be 9.0											5 B 10.8	6 C 12.0	7 N 14.0	8 O 16.0	9 F 19.0	10 Ne 20.2
11 Na 23.0	12 Mg 24.3											13 Al 27.0	14 Si 28.1	15 P 31.0	16 S 32.1	17 Cl 35.5	18 Ar 39.9
19 K 39.1	20 Ca 40.1	21 Sc 45.0	22 Ti 47.9	23 V 50.9	24 Cr 52.0	25 Mn 54.9	26 Fe 55.8	27 Co 58.9	28 Ni 58.7	29 Cu 63.5	30 Zn 65.4	31 Ga 69.7	32 Ge 72.6	33 As 74.9	34 Se 79.0	35 Br 79.9	36 Kr 83.8
37 Rb 85.5	38 Sr 87.6	39 Y 88.9	40 Zr 91.2	41 Nb 92.9	42 Mo 95.9	43 Tc (98)	44 Ru 101.1	45 Rh 102.9	46 Pd 106.4	47 Ag 107.9	48 Cd 112.4	49 In 114.8	50 Sn 118.7	51 Sb 121.8	52 Te 127.6	53 I 126.9	54 Xe 131.3
55 Cs 132.9	56 Ba 137.3	57 *La 138.9	72 Hf 178.5	73 Ta 180.9	74 W 183.9	75 Re 186.2	76 Os 190.2	77 Ir 192.2	78 Pt 195.1	79 Au 197.0	80 Hg 200.6	81 Tl 204.4	82 Pb 207.2	83 Bi 209.0	84 Po (209)	85 At (210)	86 Rn (222)
87 Fr (223)	88 Ra 226.0	89 †Ac 227.0	104 Rf (261)	105 Db (262)	106 Sg (266)	107 Bh (264)	108 Hs (277)	109 Mt (268)	110 Ds (281)	111 Rg (272)	112 Cn (285)	113 Uut (286)	114 Fl (289)	115 Uup (288)	116 Lv (293)	117 Uus (294)	118 Uuo (294)

*Lanthanide Series:	58 Ce 140.1	59 Pr 140.9	60 Nd 144.2	61 Pm (145)	62 Sm 150.4	63 Eu 152.0	64 Gd 157.3	65 Tb 158.9	66 Dy 162.5	67 Ho 164.9	68 Er 167.3	69 Tm 168.9	70 Yb 173.0	71 Lu 175.0
†Actinide Series:	90 Th 232.0	91 Pa (231)	92 U 238.0	93 Np (237)	94 Pu (244)	95 Am (243)	96 Cm (247)	97 Bk (247)	98 Cf (251)	99 Es (252)	100 Fm (257)	101 Md (258)	102 No (259)	103 Lr (260)

Periodic Table of the Elements

4.1 ATOMS

The smallest unit of any element is one **atom** of the element. All atoms have a central **nucleus,** which contains **protons** and **neutrons,** known collectively as **nucleons.** Each proton has an electric charge of +1 elementary unit; neutrons have no charge. Outside the nucleus, an atom contains electrons, and each **electron** has a charge of –1 elementary unit.

In every neutral atom, the number of electrons outside the nucleus is equal to the number of protons inside the nucleus. The electrons are held in the atom by the electrostatic attraction of the positively charged nucleus.

The number of protons in the nucleus of an atom is called its **atomic number,** Z. The atomic number of an atom uniquely determines what element the atom is, and Z may be shown explicitly by a subscript before the symbol of the element. For example, every beryllium atom contains exactly four protons, and we can write this as ${}_4\text{Be}$.

A proton and a neutron each have a mass slightly more than one atomic mass unit (1 amu = 1.66×10^{-27} kg), and an electron has a mass that's only about 0.05 percent the mass of either a proton or a neutron. So, virtually all the mass of an atom is due to the mass of the nucleus.

The number of protons plus the number of neutrons in the nucleus of an atom gives the atom's **mass number,** A. If we let N stand for the number of neutrons, then $A = Z + N$.

In designating a particular atom of an element, we refer to its mass number. One way to do this is to write A as a superscript. For example, if a beryllium atom contains 5 neutrons, then its mass number is 4 + 5 = 9, and we would write this as ${}^9_4\text{Be}$ or simply as ${}^9\text{Be}$. Another way is simply to write the mass number after the name of the elements, with a hyphen; ${}^9\text{Be}$ is beryllium-9.

4.2 ISOTOPES

If two atoms of the same element differ in their numbers of neutrons, then they are called **isotopes.** The atoms shown below are two different isotopes of the element beryllium. The atom on the left has 4 protons and 3 neutrons, so its mass number is 7; it's ^{7}Be (or beryllium-7). The atom on the right has 4 protons and 5 neutrons, so it's ^{9}Be (beryllium-9).

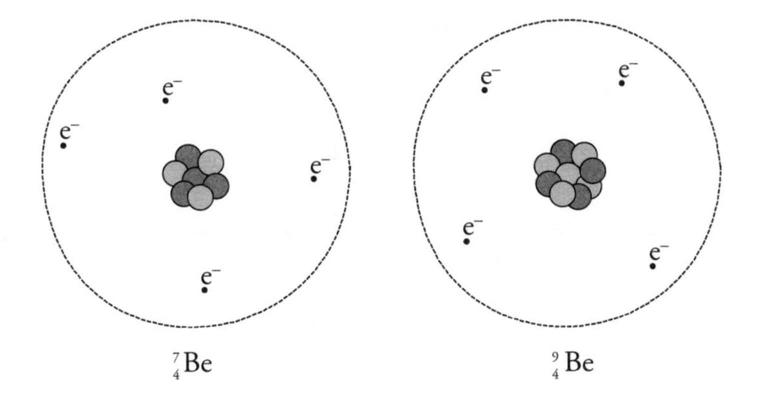

(These figures are definitely not to scale. If they were, each dashed circle showing the "outer edge" of the atom would literally be about 1500 m—almost a mile across! The nucleus occupies only the *tiniest* fraction of an atom's volume, which is mostly empty space.) Notice that these atoms—like all isotopes of a given element—*have the same atomic number but different mass numbers.*

Example 4-1: An atom with 7 neutrons and a mass number of 12 is an isotope of what element?

A) Boron
B) Nitrogen
C) Magnesium
D) Potassium

Solution: If $A = 12$ and $N = 7$, then $Z = A - N = 12 - 7 = 5$. The element with an atomic number of 5 is boron. Therefore, choice A is the answer.

Atomic Weight

Elements exist naturally as a collection of their isotopes. The **atomic weight of an element** is a *weighted average* of the masses of its naturally occurring isotopes. For example, boron has two naturally occurring isotopes: boron-10, with an atomic mass of 10.013 amu, and boron-11, with an atomic mass of 11.009 amu. Since boron-10 accounts for 20 percent of all naturally occurring boron, and boron-11 accounts for the other 80 percent, the atomic weight of boron is

$$(20\%)(10.013 \text{ amu}) + (80\%)(11.009 \text{ amu}) = 10.810 \text{ amu}$$

and this is the value listed in the periodic table. (Recall that the atomic mass unit is defined so that the most abundant isotope of carbon, carbon-12, has a mass of precisely 12 amu.)

4.3 IONS

When a neutral atom gains or loses electrons, it becomes charged, and the resulting atom is called an **ion**. For each electron it gains, an atom acquires a charge of –1 unit, and for each electron it loses, an atom acquires a charge of +1 unit. A negatively charged ion is called an **anion**, while a positively charged ion is called a **cation**.

We designate how many electrons an atom has gained or lost by placing this number as a superscript after the chemical symbol for the element. For example, if a lithium atom loses 1 electron, it becomes the lithium cation Li^{1+}, or simply Li^{+}. If a phosphorus atom gains 3 electrons, it becomes the phosphorus anion P^{3-}, or phosphide.

Example 4-2: An atom contains 16 protons, 17 neutrons, and 18 electrons. Which of the following best indicates this ion?

A) $^{33}Cl^{-}$
B) $^{34}Cl^{-}$
C) $^{33}S^{2-}$
D) $^{34}S^{2-}$

Solution: Any nucleus that contains 16 protons is sulfur, so we can eliminate choices A and B immediately. Now, because $Z = 16$ and $N = 17$, the mass number, A, is $Z + N = 16 + 17 = 33$. Therefore, the answer is C.

Example 4-3: Of the following atoms/ions, which one contains the greatest number of neutrons?

A) $^{60}_{28}Ni$

B) $^{64}_{29}Cu^{+}$

C) $^{64}_{30}Zn$

D) $^{64}_{30}Zn^{2+}$

Solution: To find N, we just subtract Z (the subscript) from A (the superscript). The atom in choice A has $N = 60 - 28 = 32$; the ion in choice B has $N = 64 - 29 = 35$, and the atom or ion in both choices C and D have $N = 64 - 30 = 34$. Therefore, of the choices given, the ion in choice B contains the greatest number of neutrons.

4.4 NUCLEAR STABILITY AND RADIOACTIVITY

The protons and neutrons in a nucleus are held together by a force called the **strong nuclear force**. It's stronger than the electrical force between charged particles, since for all atoms besides hydrogen, the strong nuclear force must overcome the electrical repulsion between the protons. In fact, of the four fundamental forces of nature, the strong nuclear force is the most powerful even though it only works over extremely short distances, as seen in the nucleus.

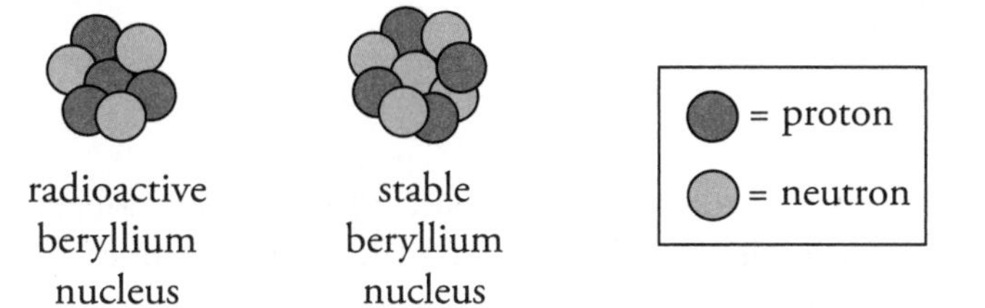

Unstable nuclei are said to be **radioactive**, and they undergo a transformation to make them more stable, altering the number and ratio of protons and neutrons or just lowering their energy. Such a process is called **radioactive decay**, and we'll look at three types: **alpha**, **beta** and **gamma**. The nucleus that undergoes radioactive decay is known as the **parent**, and the resulting more stable nucleus is known as the **daughter**.

Alpha Decay

When a large nucleus wants to become more stable by reducing the number of protons and neutrons, it emits an alpha particle. An **alpha particle**, denoted by ${}^{4}_{2}\alpha$, consists of 2 protons and 2 neutrons:

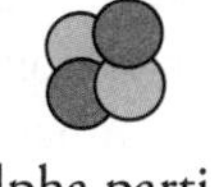

alpha particle

This is equivalent to a helium-4 nucleus, so an alpha particle can also be denoted by ${}^{4}_{2}\text{He}$. Alpha decay reduces the parent's atomic number by 2 and the mass number by 4. For example, polonium-210 is an α-emitter. It undergoes alpha decay to form the stable nucleus lead-206:

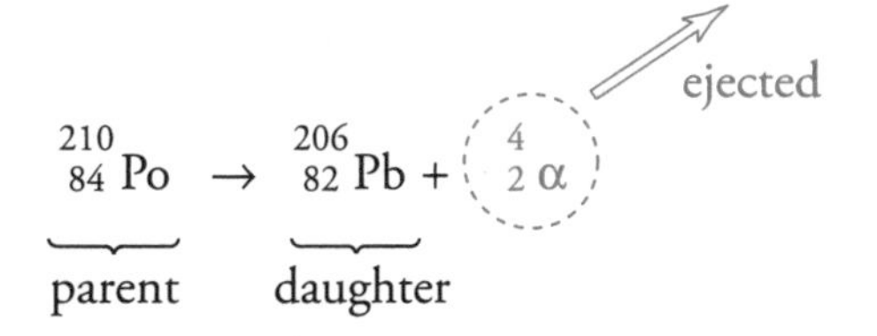

Although alpha particles are emitted with high energy from the parent nucleus, this energy is quickly lost as the particle travels through matter or air. As a result, the particles do not typically travel far, and can be stopped by the outer layers of human skin or a piece of paper.

Beta Decay

There are actually three types of beta decay: β^-, β^+, and electron capture. Each type of beta decay involves the conversion of a neutron into a proton (along with some other particles that are beyond the scope of the MCAT), or vice versa, through the action of the **weak nuclear force**.

Beta particles are more dangerous than alpha particles since they are significantly less massive. They therefore have more energy and a greater penetrating ability. However, they can be stopped by aluminum foil or a centimeter of plastic or glass.

β^- Decay

When an unstable nucleus contains too many neutrons, it may convert a neutron into a proton and an electron (also known as a **β^- particle**), which is ejected. The atomic number of the resulting daughter nucleus is 1 greater than the radioactive parent nucleus, but the mass number remains the same. The isotope carbon-14, the decay of which is the basis of radiocarbon dating of archaeological artifacts, is an example of a radioactive nucleus that undergoes β^- decay:

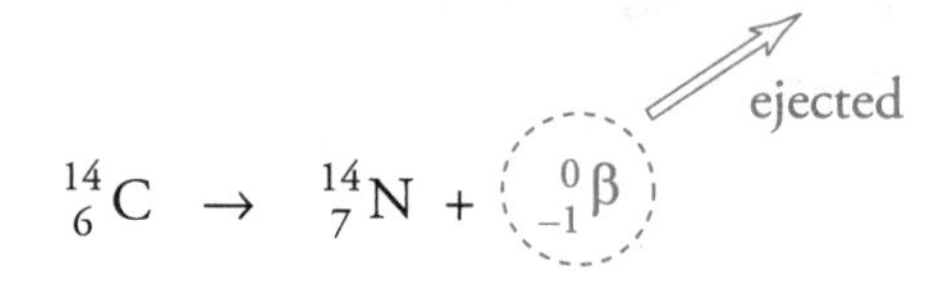

β^- decay is the most common type of beta decay, and when the MCAT mentions "beta decay" without any further qualification, it means β^- decay.

β^+ Decay (or Positron Emission)

When an unstable nucleus contains too few neutrons, it converts a proton into a neutron and a positron, which is ejected. This is known as **β^+ decay**. The positron is the electron's *antiparticle*; it's identical to an electron except its charge is positive. The atomic number of the resulting daughter nucleus is 1 less than the radioactive parent nucleus, but the mass number remains the same. The isotope fluorine-18, which can be used in medical diagnostic bone scans in the form $Na^{18}F$, is an example of a positron emitter:

ejected

$$^{18}_{9}F \rightarrow {}^{18}_{8}O + {}^{0}_{+1}\beta$$

Electron Capture

Another way for an unstable nucleus to increase its number of neutrons is to capture an electron from the closest electron shell (the $n = 1$ shell) and use it in the conversion of a proton into a neutron. Just like positron emission, **electron capture** causes the atomic number to be reduced by 1 while the mass number remains the same. The nucleus chromium-51 is an example of a radioactive nucleus that undergoes electron capture, becoming the stable nucleus vanadium-51:

$$^{51}_{24}\text{Cr} + {}^{0}_{-1}\text{e}^{-} \rightarrow {}^{51}_{23}\text{V}$$

Gamma Decay

A nucleus in an excited energy state—which is usually the case after a nucleus has undergone alpha or any type of beta decay—can "relax" to its ground state by emitting energy in the form of one or more photons of electromagnetic radiation. These photons are called **gamma photons** (symbolized by γ) and have a very high frequency and energy. Gamma photons (or gamma rays) have neither mass nor charge, and can therefore penetrate matter most effectively. A few inches of lead or about a meter of concrete will stop most gamma rays. Their ejection from a radioactive atom changes neither the atomic number nor the mass number of the nucleus. For example, after silicon-31 undergoes β^- decay, the resulting daughter nucleus then undergoes gamma decay:

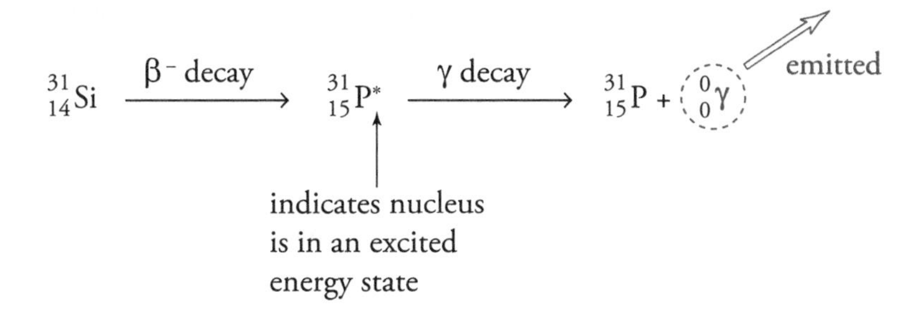

Notice that alpha and beta decay change the identity of the nucleus, but gamma decay does not. Gamma decay is simply an expulsion of energy.

Summary of Radioactive Decay

$N\downarrow\ Z\downarrow$	Alpha Decay	Decreases the number of neutrons *and* protons in large nucleus Subtracts 4 from the mass number Subtracts 2 from the atomic number ${}^{A}_{Z}\text{X} \xrightarrow{\alpha} {}^{A-4}_{Z-2}\text{Y} + {}^{4}_{2}\alpha$
$N\downarrow\ Z\uparrow$	Beta⁻ Decay	Decreases the number of neutrons, increases the number of protons Adds 1 to the atomic number ${}^{A}_{Z}\text{X} \xrightarrow{\beta^-} {}_{Z+1}^{\ \ A}\text{Y} + {}^{\ 0}_{-1}\beta$
$N\uparrow\ Z\downarrow$	Positron Emission	Increases the number of neutrons, decreases the number of protons Subtracts 1 from the atomic number ${}^{A}_{Z}\text{X} \xrightarrow{\beta^+} {}_{Z-1}^{\ \ A}\text{Y} + {}^{\ 0}_{+1}\beta$
$N\uparrow\ Z\downarrow$	Electron Capture	Increases the number of neutrons, decreases the number of protons Subtracts 1 from the atomic number ${}^{A}_{Z}\text{X} + {}^{\ 0}_{-1}\text{e}^- \xrightarrow{\text{EC}} {}_{Z-1}^{\ \ A}\text{Y}$
	Gamma Decay	Brings an excited nucleus to a lower energy state Doesn't change mass number or atomic number ${}^{A}_{Z}\text{X}^* \xrightarrow{\gamma} {}^{A}_{Z}\text{X} + {}^{0}_{0}\gamma$

Example 4-4: Radioactive calcium-47, a known β^- emitter, is administered in the form of $^{47}CaCl_2$ by I.V. as a diagnostic tool to study calcium metabolism. What is the daughter nucleus of ^{47}Ca?

A) ^{46}K
B) ^{47}K
C) $^{47}Ca^+$
D) ^{47}Sc

Solution: Since β^- decay will always change the identity of an element, eliminate choice C. The β^- decay of ^{47}Ca is described by this nuclear reaction:

$$ {}^{47}_{20}\text{Ca} \rightarrow {}^{47}_{21}\text{Sc} + {}^{\ 0}_{-1}\beta $$

Therefore, the daughter nucleus is scandium-47, choice D.

Example 4-5: Americium-241 is used to provide intracavitary radiation for the treatment of malignancies. This radioisotope is known to undergo alpha decay. What is the daughter nucleus?

A) ^{237}Np
B) ^{241}Pu
C) ^{237}Bk
D) ^{243}Bk

Solution: Alpha decay will reduce the mass by 4, to 237, so eliminate choices B and D. It will reduce the nuclear charge by 2 from 95 to 93, so choose A. The α decay of ^{241}Am is described by this nuclear reaction:

$$^{241}_{95}\text{Am} \rightarrow ^{237}_{93}\text{Np} + ^{4}_{2}\alpha$$

Example 4-6: Vitamin B_{12} can be prepared with *radioactive* cobalt (^{58}Co), a known β^+ emitter, and administered orally as a diagnostic tool to test for defects in intestinal vitamin B_{12} absorption. What is the daughter nucleus of ^{58}Co?

A) ^{57}Fe
B) ^{58}Fe
C) ^{59}Co
D) ^{59}Ni

Solution: All types of β^+ decay leave the mass of the daughter and parent elements the same, thus the mass must be 58, making choice B the only option. The β^+ decay of ^{58}Co is described by this nuclear reaction:

$$^{58}_{27}\text{Co} \rightarrow ^{58}_{26}\text{Fe} + ^{0}_{+1}\beta$$

Example 4-7: A certain radioactive isotope is administered orally as a diagnostic tool to study pancreatic function and intestinal fat absorption. This radioisotope is known to undergo β^- decay, and the daughter nucleus is xenon-131. What is the parent radioisotope?

A) ^{131}Cs
B) ^{131}I
C) ^{132}I
D) ^{132}Xe

Solution: Eliminate choices C and D since the mass number should remain the same for all forms of β^- decay. The β^- decay that results in ^{131}Xe is described by this nuclear reaction:

$$^{131}_{53}\text{I} \rightarrow ^{131}_{54}\text{Xe} + ^{0}_{-1}\beta$$

Therefore, the parent nucleus is iodine-131, choice B.

Example 4-8: Which of these modes of radioactive decay causes a change in the mass number of the parent nucleus?

A) α
B) β^-
C) β^+
D) γ

Solution: Gamma decay causes no changes in the number of protons or neutrons, so we can eliminate choice D. Beta decay (β^-, β^+, and EC) changes both N and Z by 1, but always such that the change in the sum $N + Z$ (which is the mass number, A) is zero. Therefore, we can eliminate choices B and C. The answer is A.

Example 4-9: One of the naturally occurring radioactive series begins with radioactive ^{238}U. It undergoes a series of decays, one of which is: alpha, beta, beta, alpha, alpha, alpha, alpha, alpha, beta, beta, alpha, beta, alpha, beta. What is the final resulting nuclide of this series of decays?

A) ^{204}Pb
B) ^{204}Pt
C) ^{206}Pb
D) ^{206}Pt

Solution: Since there are so many individual decays, let's find the final daughter nucleus using a simple shortcut: For every alpha decay, we'll subtract 4 from the mass number (the superscript) and subtract 2 from the atomic number (the subscript); for every beta decay, we'll add 0 to the mass number and 1 to the atomic number. Since there are a total of 8 alpha-decays and 6 beta-decays, we get

$$^{238}_{92}U \xrightarrow{8\alpha} {}^{238-8(4)}_{92-8(2)} \xrightarrow{6\beta^-} {}^{+6(0)}_{+6(1)} = {}^{206}_{82}Pb$$

Therefore, the final daughter nucleus is lead-206, choice C.

Half-Life

Different radioactive nuclei decay at different rates. The **half-life**, which is denoted by $t_{1/2}$, of a radioactive substance is the time it takes for one-half of some sample of the substance to decay. Thus, the shorter the half-life, the faster the decay. The amount of a radioactive substance decreases exponentially with time, as illustrated in the following graph.

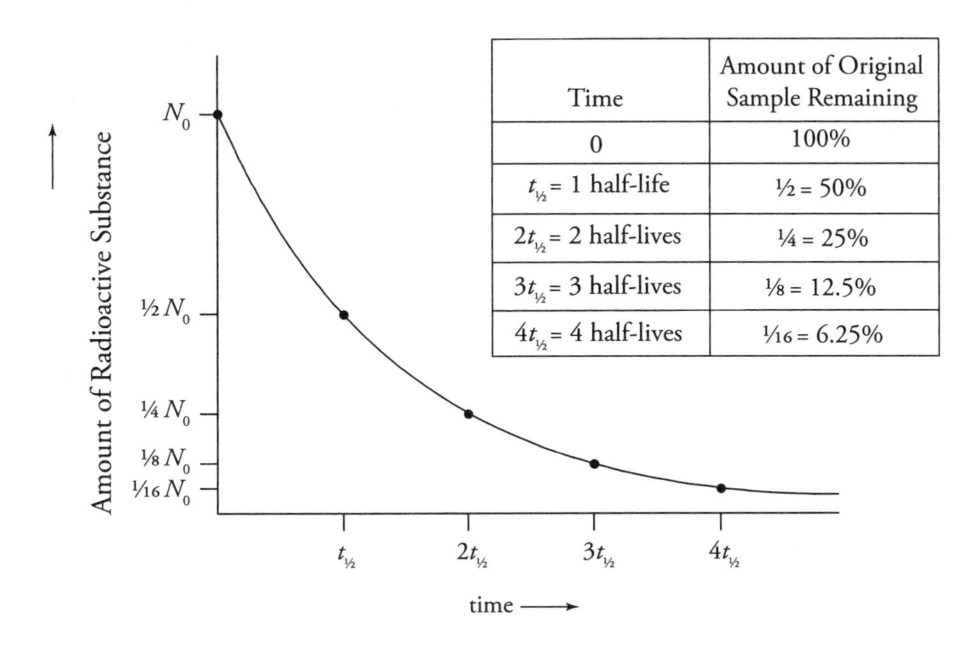

Time	Amount of Original Sample Remaining
0	100%
$t_{½}$ = 1 half-life	½ = 50%
$2t_{½}$ = 2 half-lives	¼ = 25%
$3t_{½}$ = 3 half-lives	⅛ = 12.5%
$4t_{½}$ = 4 half-lives	1/16 = 6.25%

For example, a radioactive sample with an initial mass of 80 grams and a half-life of 6 years will decay as follows:

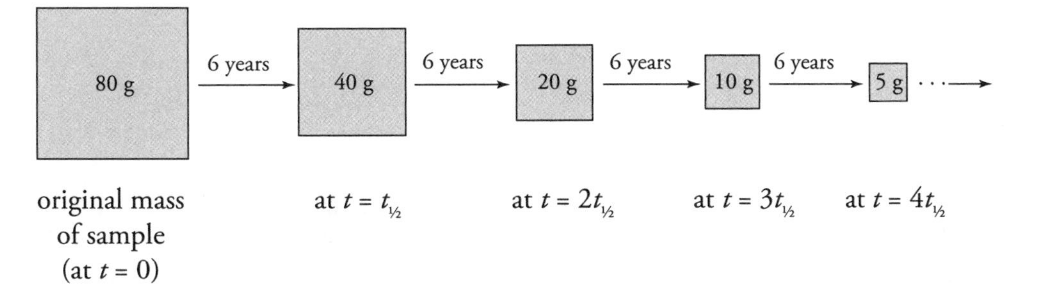

The equation for the exponential decay curve shown above is often written as $N = N_0e^{-kt}$, but a simpler—and much more intuitive way—is

$$N = N_0(1/2)^{T/t_{1/2}}$$

where $t_{1/2}$ is the half-life and T is the total time the sample has decayed. For example, when $T = 3t_{1/2}$, the number of radioactive nuclei remaining, N, is $N_0(1/2)^3 = 1/8N_0$, just what we expect. If the form N_0e^{-kt} is used, the value of k (known as the **decay constant**) is inversely proportional to the half-life: $k = (\ln 2)/t_{1/2}$. The shorter the half-life, the greater the decay constant, and the more rapidly the sample decays.

Example 4-10: Cesium-137 has a half-life of 30 years. How long will it take for only 0.3 g to remain from a sample that had an original mass of 2.4 g?

A) 60 years
B) 90 years
C) 120 years
D) 240 years

Solution: Since 0.3 grams is 1/8 of 2.4 grams, the question is asking how long it will take for the radioisotope to decrease to 1/8 its original amount. We know that this requires 3 half-lives, since $1/2 \times 1/2 \times 1/2 = 1/8$. So, if each half-life is 30 years, then 3 half-lives will be 3(30) = 90 years, choice B.

Example 4-11: Radiolabeled vitamin B_{12} containing radioactive cobalt-58 is administered to diagnose a defect in a patient's vitamin-B_{12} absorption. If ^{58}Co has a half-life of 72 days, approximately what percentage of the radioisotope will still remain in the patient a year later?

A) 3%
B) 5%
C) 8%
D) 10%

Solution: One year is approximately equal to 5 half-lives of this radioisotope, since $5 \times 72 = 360$ days = 1 year. After 5 half-lives, the amount of the radioisotope will drop to $(1/2)^5 = 1/32$ of the original amount administered. Because 1/32 = 3/100 = 3%, the best answer is choice A.

Example: 4-12 Iodinated oleic acid, containing radioactive iodine-131, is administered orally to study a patient's pancreatic function. If ^{131}I has a half-life of 8 days, how long after the procedure will the amount of ^{131}I remaining in the patient's body be reduced to 1/5 its initial value?

A) 19 days
B) 32 days
C) 40 days
D) 256 days

Solution: Although the fraction 1/5 is not a whole-number power of 1/2, we do know that it's between 1/4 and 1/8. If 1/4 of the sample were left, we'd know that 2 half-lives had elapsed, and if 1/8 of the sample were left, we'd know that 3 half-lives had elapsed. Therefore, because 1/5 is between 1/4 and 1/8, we know that the amount of time will be between 2 and 3 half-lives. Since each half-life is 8 days, this amount of time will be between 2(8) = 16 days and 3(8) = 24 days. Of the choices given, only choice A is in this range.

Nuclear Binding Energy

Every nucleus that contains protons *and* neutrons has a **nuclear binding energy**. This is the energy that was released when the individual nucleons (protons and neutrons) were bound together by the strong force to form the nucleus. It's also equal to the energy that would be required to break up the intact nucleus into its individual nucleons. The greater the binding energy per nucleon, the more stable the nucleus.

When nucleons bind together to form a nucleus, some mass is converted to energy, so the mass of the combined nucleus is *less* than the sum of the masses of all its nucleons individually. The difference, Δm, is called the **mass defect**, and its energy equivalent *is* the nuclear binding energy. For a stable nucleus, the mass defect,

$$\Delta m = (\text{total mass of separate nucleons}) - (\text{mass of nucleus})$$

will always be positive.

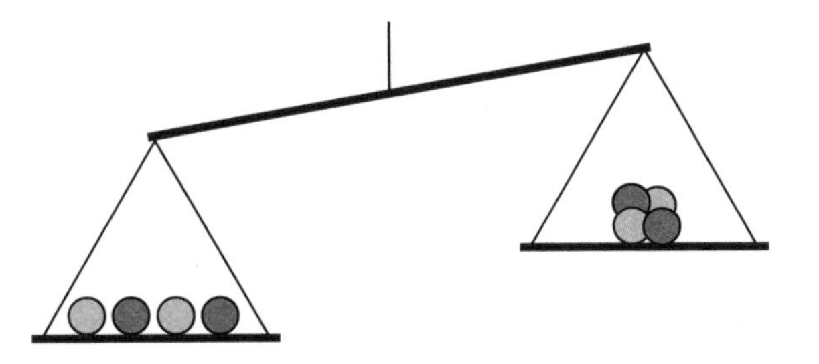

The nuclear binding energy, E_B, can be found from the mass defect using **Einstein's equations for mass-energy equivalence:** $E_B = (\Delta m)c^2$, where c is the speed of light (3×10^8 m/s). If mass is measured in kilograms and energy in Joules, then 1 kg $\leftrightarrow$ 9×10^{16} J. But in the nuclear domain, masses are often expressed in atomic mass units (1 amu $\approx$ 1.66×10^{-27} kg), and energy is expressed in **electronvolts** (1 eV $\approx$ 1.6×10^{-19} J). In terms of these units, the equations for the nuclear binding energy, $E_B = (\Delta m)c^2$, can be written as E_B (in eV) = [Δm(in amu)] $\times$ 931.5 MeV.

Example 4-13: The mass defect of a helium nucleus is 5×10^{-29} kg. What is its nuclear binding energy?

Solution: The equation $E_B = (\Delta m)c^2$ implies that 1 kg $\leftrightarrow$ 9×10^{16} J, so a mass defect of 5×10^{-29} kg is equivalent to an energy of (5×10^{-29} kg)(9×10^{16} J) = 4.5×10^{-12} J. (For practice, check that this binding energy is approximately equal to 30 MeV.)

Example 4-14: The mass defect of a triton (the nucleus of a tritium, $^3_1$H) is about 0.009 amu. What is its nuclear binding energy, in electronvolts?

Solution: In terms of amus and electronvolts, the equation for the nuclear binding energy is E_B(in eV) = [Δm(in amu)] $\times$ 931.5 MeV. Therefore, for the tritium nucleus, we have

$$E_b = (0.009) \times (931.5 \text{ MeV}) \approx 8.4 \text{ MeV}$$

4.5 ATOMIC STRUCTURE

Emission Spectra

Imagine a glass tube filled with a small sample of an element in gaseous form. When electric current is passed through the tube, the gas begins to glow with a color characteristic of that particular element. If this light emitted by the gas is then passed through a prism—which will separate the light into its component wavelengths—the result is the element's **emission spectrum.**

An atom's emission spectrum gives an energetic "fingerprint" of that element because it consists of a unique sequence of *bright* lines that correspond to specific wavelengths and energies. The energies of the photons, or particles of light that are emitted, are related to their frequencies, f, and wavelengths, λ, by the equation

$$E_{photon} = hf = h\frac{c}{\lambda}$$

where h is a universal constant called **Planck's constant** (6.63×10^{-34} J·s) and c is the speed of light. For the following discussion, a general understanding of the electromagnetic spectrum will be useful. More detail on this topic can be found in Section 13.1 of the *MCAT Physics Review.*

The Bohr Model of the Atom

In 1913 the Danish physicist Niels Bohr realized that the model of atomic structure of his time was inconsistent with emission spectral data. In order to account for the limited numbers of lines that are observed in the emission spectra of elements, Bohr described a new model of the atom. In this model that would later take his name, he proposed that the electrons in an atom orbited the nucleus in circular paths, much as the planets orbit the sun in the solar system. Distance from the nucleus was related to the energy of the electrons; electrons with greater amounts of energy orbited the nucleus at greater distances. However, the electrons in the atom cannot assume any arbitrary energy, but have *quantized* energy states, and thereby only orbit at certain allowed distances from the nucleus.

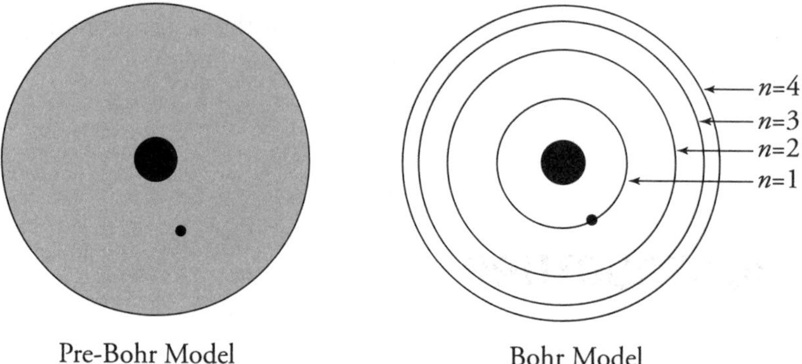

Pre-Bohr Model
Electrons assume arbitrary energies

Bohr Model
Electrons assume discrete energies

If an electron absorbs energy that's exactly equal to the difference in energy between its current level and that of an available higher lever, it "jumps" to that higher level. The electron can then "drop" to a lower energy level, emitting a photon with an energy exactly equal to the difference between the levels. This model predicted that elements would have line spectra instead of continuous spectra, as would be the case if transitions between all possible energies could be expected. An electron could only gain or lose very specific amounts of energy due to the quantized nature of the energy levels. Therefore, only photons with certain energies are observed. These specific energies corresponded to very specific wavelengths, as seen in the emission line spectra.

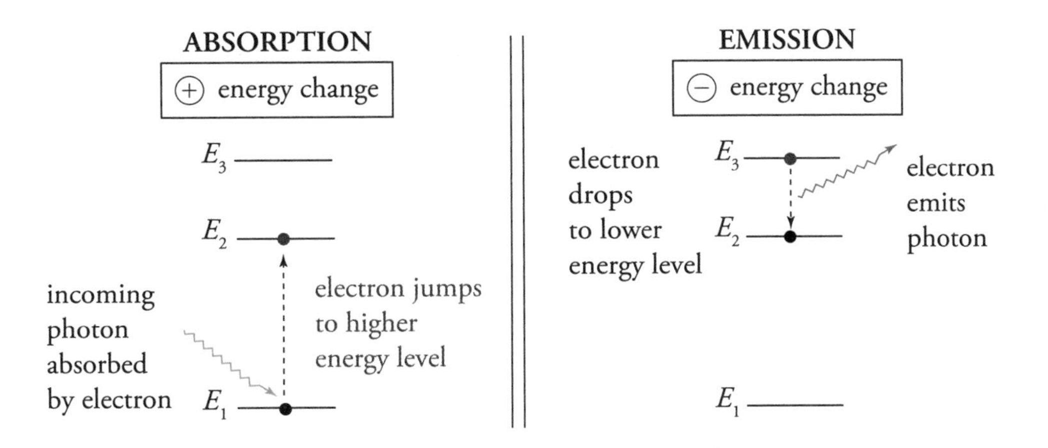

In the transition depicted below, an electron is initially in its **ground state** ($n = 1$), or its lowest possible energy level. When this electron absorbs a photon it jumps to a higher energy level, known as an **excited state** (in this case $n = 3$). Electrons excited to high energy don't always relax to the ground state in large jumps, rather they can relax in a series of smaller jumps, gradually coming back to the ground state. From this excited state the electron can relax in one of two ways, either dropping into the $n = 2$ level, or directly back to the $n = 1$ ground state. In the first scenario, we can expect to detect a photon with energy corresponding to the difference between $n = 3$ and $n = 2$. In the latter case we'd detect a more energetic photon of energy corresponding to the difference between $n = 3$ and $n = 1$.

Note: Distances between energy levels are not drawn to scale.

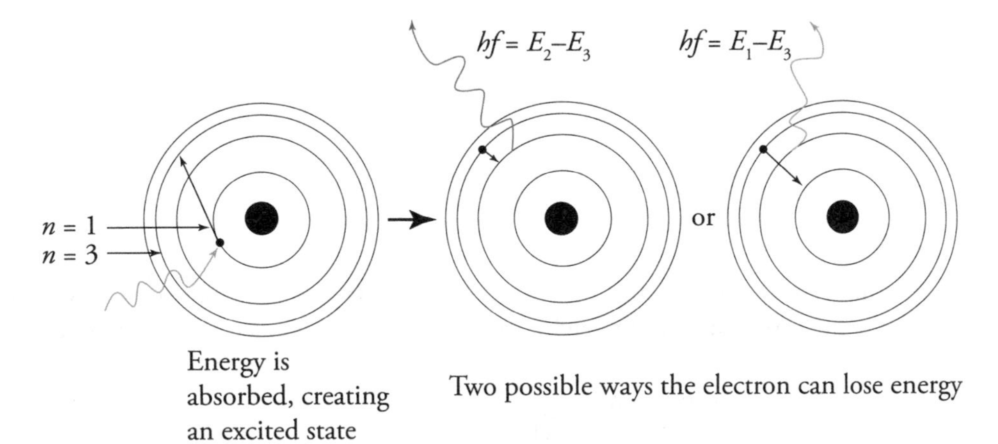

The energies of these discrete energy levels were given by Bohr in the following equation, which only accurately predicted the behavior of atoms or ions containing one electron, now known as Bohr atoms. The value n in this case represents the energy level of the electron.

$$E_n = \frac{(-2.178 \times 10^{-18}\ \text{J})}{n^2}$$

Since we can calculate the energies of the levels of a Bohr atom, we can predict the wavelengths of photons emitted or absorbed when electrons transition between any two energy levels. To do this we calculate the energy differences between discrete levels by subtracting the initial energy of the electron from the final energy of the electron. We can find the energies of the two possible emitted photons shown above as follows:

$$\Delta E_{3\to 2} = \frac{(-2.178\times 10^{-18}\,\text{J})}{(2)^2} - \frac{(-2.178\times 10^{-18}\,\text{J})}{(3)^2}$$

$$\Delta E_{3\to 2} = -3.025\times 10^{-19}\,\text{J}$$

$$\Delta E_{3\to 1} = \frac{(-2.178\times 10^{-18}\,\text{J})}{(1)^2} - \frac{(-2.178\times 10^{-18}\,\text{J})}{(3)^2}$$

$$\Delta E_{3\to 1} = -1.936\times 10^{-18}\,\text{J}$$

Note that both energies calculated above are negative, indicating that energy is being released by the electron as it falls from its excited state to a lower energy level. For electron transitions from the ground state to an excited state, the ΔE values will be positive, indicating energy is absorbed by the electron.

Once the energy is calculated, the wavelength of the photon can be found by employing the relation $\Delta E = h\frac{c}{\lambda}$. Not all electron transitions produce photons we can see with the naked eye, but all transitions in an atom will produce photons either in the ultraviolet, visible, or infrared region of the electromagnetic spectrum.

Example 4-15: Which of the following is NOT an example of a Bohr atom?

A) H
B) He^{+}
C) Li^{2+}
D) H^{+}

Solution: A Bohr atom is one that contains only one electron. Since H^{+} has a positive charge from losing the one electron in the neutral atom thereby having no electrons at all, choice D is the answer.

Example 4-16: The first four electron energy levels of an atom are shown at the right, given in terms of electron volts. Which of the following gives the energy of a photon that could NOT be emitted by this atom?

$E_4 = -18$ eV

$E_3 = -32$ eV

$E_2 = -72$ eV

$E_1 = -288$ eV

A) 14 eV
B) 40 eV
C) 44 eV
D) 54 eV

Solution: The difference between E_4 and E_3 is 14 eV, so a photon of 14 eV would be emitted if an electron were to drop from level 4 to level 3; this eliminates choice A. Similarly, the difference between E_3 and E_2 is 40 eV, so choice B is eliminated, and the difference between E_4 and E_2 is 54 eV, so choice D is eliminated. The answer must be C; no two energy levels in this atom are separated by 44 eV.

Example 4-17: Consider two electron transitions. In the first case, an electron falls from $n = 4$ to $n = 2$, giving off a photon of light with a wavelength equal to 488 nm. In the second transition, an electron moves from $n = 3$ to $n = 4$. For this transition, we would expect that:

A) energy is emitted, and the wavelength of the corresponding photon will be shorter than the first transition.
B) energy is emitted, and the wavelength of the corresponding photon will be longer than the first transition.
C) energy is absorbed, and the wavelength of the corresponding photon will be shorter than the first transition.
D) energy is absorbed, and the wavelength of the corresponding photon will be longer than the first transition.

Solution: Since the electron is moving from a lower to higher energy level, we would expect that the atom absorbs energy (eliminating choices A and B). Since the electron transitions between energy levels that are closer together, the ΔE between levels is smaller. By the $\Delta E = h\frac{c}{\lambda}$ relationship, we know that energy and wavelength are inversely related. Therefore with a smaller energy change, the wavelength of the associated light will be longer. D is the correct answer.

The Quantum Model of the Atom

While one-electron atoms produce easily predicted atomic spectra, the Bohr model does not do a good job of predicting the atomic spectra of many-electron atoms. This shows that the Bohr model cannot describe the electron-electron interactions that exist in many-electron atoms. The quantum model of the atom was developed to account for these differences. Bohr's model suggested, and we still hold to be true, that electrons held by an atom can exist only at discrete energy levels—that is, electron energy levels are quantized. This quantization is described by a unique "address" for each electron, consisting of four quantum numbers designating the shell, subshell, orbital, and spin. While the details of quantum numbers are beyond the scope of the MCAT, it is still useful to understand the conceptual basis of the quantum model.

The Energy Shell

The energy shell (n) of an electron in the quantum model of the atom is analogous to the circular orbits in the Bohr model of the atom. An electron in a higher shell has a greater amount of energy and a greater average distance from the nucleus. For example, an electron in the 3rd shell ($n = 3$) has higher energy than an electron in the 2nd shell (where $n = 2$), which has more energy than an electron in the 1st shell ($n = 1$).

The Energy Subshell

In the quantum model of the atom, however, we no longer describe the path of electrons around the nucleus as circular orbits, but focus on the probability of finding an electron somewhere in the atom. Loosely speaking, an **orbital** describes a three-dimensional region around the nucleus in which the electron is most likely to be found.

A subshell in an atom is comprised of one or more orbitals, and is denoted by a letter (*s*, *p*, *d*, or *f*) that describes the shape and energy of the orbital(s). The orbitals in the subshells get progressively more complex and higher in energy in the order listed above. Each energy shell has one or more subshells, and each higher energy shell contains one additional subshell. For example, the first energy shell contains the *s* subshell, while the second energy shell contains both the *s* and *p* subshell, etc.

The Orbital Orientation

Each subshell contains one or more orbitals of the same energy (also called degenerate orbitals), and these orbitals have different three-dimensional orientations in space. The number of orientations increases by two in each successive subshell. For example, the *s* subshell contains one orientation and the *p* subshell contains three orientations.

You should be able to recognize the shapes of the orbitals in the *s* and *p* subshells. Each *s* subshell has just one spherically symmetrical orbital.

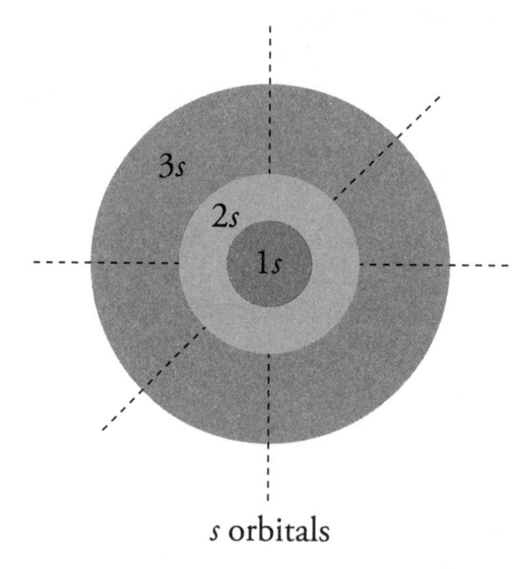

s orbitals

Each p subshell has three orbitals, each depicted as a dumbbell, with different spatial orientations.

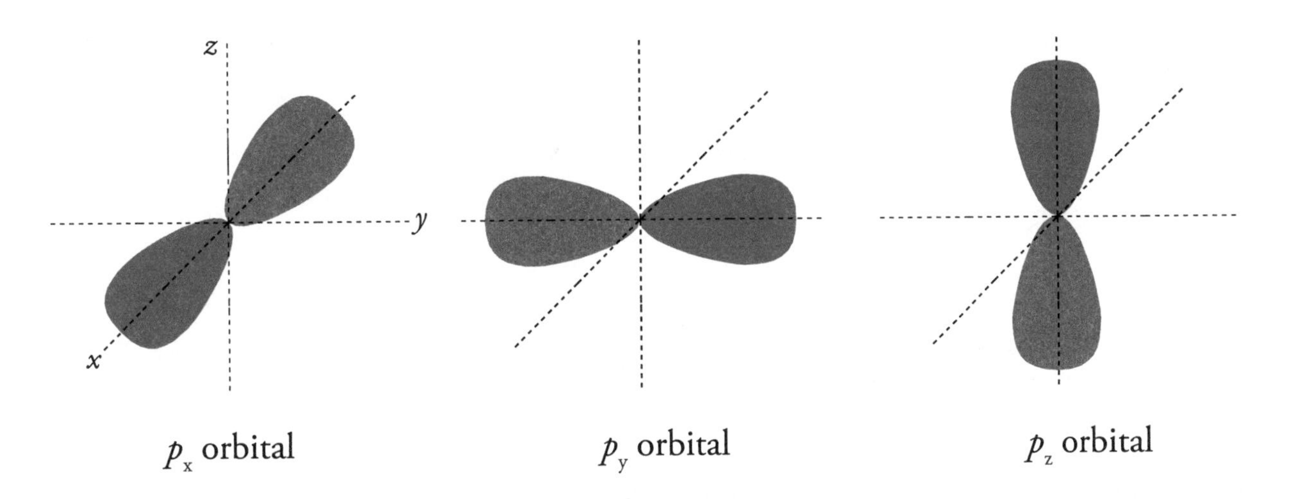

The Electron Spin

Every electron has two possible spin states, which can be considered the electron's intrinsic magnetism. Because of this every orbital can accommodate a maximum of two electrons, one spin-up and one spin-down. If an orbital is full, we say that the electrons it holds are "spin-paired."

4.6 ELECTRON CONFIGURATIONS

Now that we've described the modern quantum model of the atom, let's see how this is represented as an electron configuration. There are three basic rules:

1) *Electrons occupy the lowest energy orbitals available.* (This is the **Aufbau principle.**) Electron subshells are filled in order of increasing energy. The periodic table is logically constructed to reflect this fact, and therefore one can easily determine shell filling for specific atoms based on where they appear on the table. We will detail this in the next section on "Blocks."
2) *Electrons in the same subshell occupy available orbitals singly, before pairing up.* (This is known as **Hund's rule.**)
3) *There can be no more than two electrons in any given orbital.* (This is the **Pauli exclusion principle.**)

For example, let's describe the locations for all the electrons in an oxygen atom, which contains eight electrons. Beginning with the first, lowest energy shell, there is only one subshell (s) and only one orientation in that subshell, and there can only be two electrons in that one orbital. Therefore, these two electrons fill the only orbital in the $1s$ subshell. We write this as $1s^2$, to indicate that there are two electrons in the $1s$ subshell.

We still have six electrons left, so let's move on to the second, next highest, energy shell. There are two subshells (s and p). Since the s subshell is lower in energy than the p subshell, the next two electrons go in the $2s$ subshell, that is, $2s^2$.

For the remaining four electrons, there would be three orientations of orbitals in the *p* subshell. According to Hund's rule, we place one spin up electron in each of these three orbitals. The eighth electron now pairs up with an electron in one of the 2*p* orbitals. So, the last four electrons go in the 2*p* subshell: $2p^4$ (or more explicitly, $2p_x^{\,2}2p_y^{\,1}2p_z^{\,1}$).

The complete electron configuration for oxygen can now be written like this:

$$\text{Oxygen} = 1s^2 2s^2 2p^4$$

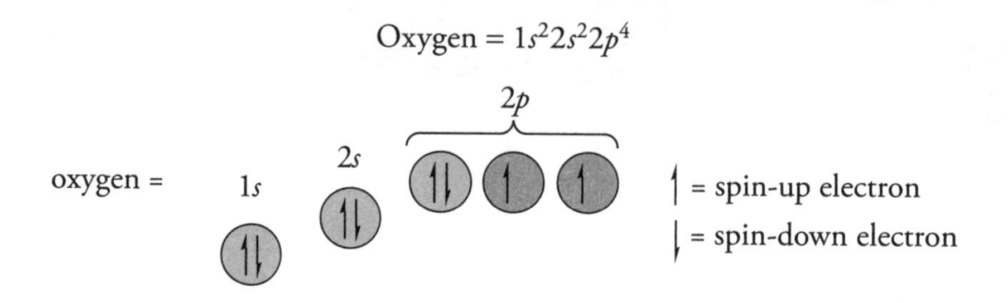

Here are the electron configurations for the first ten elements:

Z			1*s*	2*s*	2*p*		
1	Hydrogen	$1s^1$	↑				
2	Helium	$1s^2$	↑↓				
3	Lithium	$1s^2 2s^1$	↑↓	↑			
4	Beryllium	$1s^2 2s^2$	↑↓	↑↓			
5	Boron	$1s^2 2s^2 2p^1$	↑↓	↑↓	↑		
6	Carbon	$1s^2 2s^2 2p^2$	↑↓	↑↓	↑	↑	
7	Nitrogen	$1s^2 2s^2 2p^3$	↑↓	↑↓	↑	↑	↑
8	Oxygen	$1s^2 2s^2 2p^4$	↑↓	↑↓	↑↓	↑	↑
9	Fluorine	$1s^2 2s^2 2p^5$	↑↓	↑↓	↑↓	↑↓	↑
10	Neon	$1s^2 2s^2 2p^6$	↑↓	↑↓	↑↓	↑↓	↑↓

Example 4-18: What's the maximum number of electrons that can go into any *s* subshell? Any *p* subshell? Any *d*? Any *f*?

Solution: An *s* subshell has only one possible orbital orientation. Since only two electrons can fill any given orbital, an *s* subshell can hold no more than $1 \times 2 = 2$ electrons.

A *p* subshell has three possible orbital orientations (two more than an *s* subshell). Since again only two electrons can fill any given orbital, a *p* subshell can hold no more than $3 \times 2 = 6$ electrons.

A *d* subshell has five possible orbital orientations (two more than a *p* subshell). Since there are two electrons per orbital, a *d* subshell can hold no more than $5 \times 2 = 10$ electrons.

Finally, an *f* subshell has seven possible orbital orientations (two more than a *d* subshell). Since there are two electrons per orbital, an *f* subshell can hold no more than $7 \times 2 = 14$ electrons.

Example 4-19: Write down—and comment on—the electron configuration of argon (Ar, atomic number 18).

Solution: We have 18 electrons to successively place in the proper subshells, as follows:

1*s*: 2 electrons
2*s*: 2 electrons
2*p*: 6 electrons
3*s*: 2 electrons
3*p*: 6 electrons

Therefore,

$$[\text{Ar}] = 1s^2 2s^2 2p^6 3s^2 3p^6$$

Notice that 3*s* and 3*p* subshells have their full complement of electrons. In fact, the **noble gases** (those elements in the last column of the periodic table) all have their outer 8 electrons in filled subshells: 2 in the *ns* subshell plus 6 in the *np*. (The lone exception, of course, is helium; but its one and only subshell, the 1*s*, is filled—with 2 electrons.) Because their 8 valence electrons are in filled subshells, we say that these atoms—Ne, Ar, Kr, Xe, and Rn—have a complete **octet**, which accounts for their remarkable chemical stability, and lack of reactivity.

Diamagnetic and Paramagnetic Atoms

An atom that has all of its electrons spin-paired is referred to as **diamagnetic**. For example, helium, beryllium, and neon are diamagnetic. A diamagnetic atom must contain an even number of electrons and have all of its occupied subshells filled. Since all the electrons in a diamagnetic atom are spin-paired, the individual magnetic fields that they create cancel, leaving no net magnetic field. Such an atom will be *repelled* by an externally produced magnetic field.

If an atom's electrons are not all spin-paired, it is said to be **paramagnetic**. Paramagnetic atoms are *attracted* into externally produced magnetic fields.

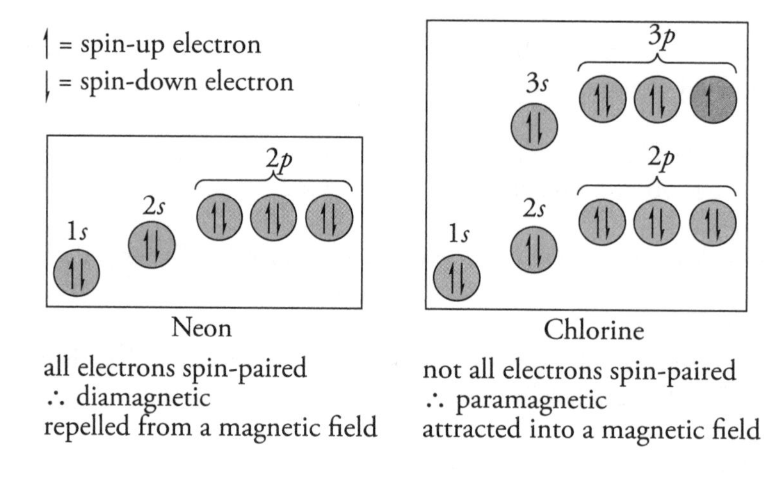

Neon

all electrons spin-paired
∴ diamagnetic
repelled from a magnetic field

Chlorine

not all electrons spin-paired
∴ paramagnetic
attracted into a magnetic field

Example 4-20: Which of the following elements is diamagnetic?

A) Sodium
B) Sulfur
C) Potassium
D) Calcium

Solution: First, a diamagnetic atom must contain an *even* number of electrons, because they all must be spin-*paired*. So, we can eliminate choices A and C, since sodium and potassium each contain an odd number of electrons (11 and 19, respectively). The electron configuration of sulfur is [Ne] $3s^23p^4$; by Hund's rule, the 4 electrons in the $3p$ subshell will look like this:

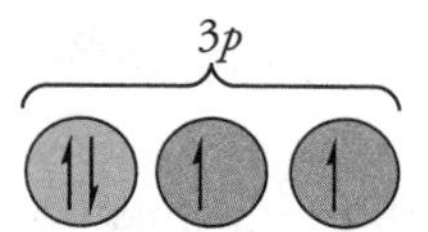

They're not all spin-paired, so sulfur is not diamagnetic. The answer must be D, calcium, because its configuration is [Ar] $4s^2$, and all of its electrons are spin-paired.

Blocks in the Periodic Table

s block → *p* block → *d* block →

	I	II											III	IV	V	VI	VII	VIII
1	1 H 1.0																	2 He 4.0
2	3 Li 6.9	4 Be 9.0											5 B 10.8	6 C 12.0	7 N 14.0	8 O 16.0	9 F 19.0	10 Ne 20.2
3	11 Na 23.0	12 Mg 24.3											13 Al 27.0	14 Si 28.1	15 P 31.0	16 S 32.1	17 Cl 35.5	18 Ar 39.9
4	19 K 39.1	20 Ca 40.1	21 Sc 45.0	22 Ti 47.9	23 V 50.9	24 Cr 52.0	25 Mn 54.9	26 Fe 55.8	27 Co 58.9	28 Ni 58.7	29 Cu 63.5	30 Zn 65.4	31 Ga 69.7	32 Ge 72.6	33 As 74.9	34 Se 79.0	35 Br 79.9	36 Kr 83.8
5	37 Rb 85.5	38 Sr 87.6	39 Y 88.9	40 Zr 91.2	41 Nb 92.9	42 Mo 95.9	43 Tc (98)	44 Ru 101.1	45 Rh 102.9	46 Pd 106.4	47 Ag 107.9	48 Cd 112.4	49 In 114.8	50 Sn 118.7	51 Sb 121.8	52 Te 127.6	53 I 126.9	54 Xe 131.3
6	55 Cs 132.9	56 Ba 137.3	57 *La 138.9	72 Hf 178.5	73 Ta 180.9	74 W 183.9	75 Re 186.2	76 Os 190.2	77 Ir 192.2	78 Pt 195.1	79 Au 197.0	80 Hg 200.6	81 Tl 204.4	82 Pb 207.2	83 Bi 209.0	84 Po (209)	85 At (210)	86 Rn (222)
7	87 Fr (223)	88 Ra 226.0	89 †Ac 227.0	104 Rf (261)	105 Db (262)	106 Sg (266)	107 Bh (264)	108 Hs (277)	109 Mt (268)	110 Ds (281)	111 Rg (272)	112 Cp (285)	113 Uut (286)	114 Fl (289)	115 Uup (288)	116 Lv (293)	117 Uus (294)	118 Uuo (294)

f block →

*Lanthanide Series:	58 Ce 140.1	59 Pr 140.9	60 Nd 144.2	61 Pm (145)	62 Sm 150.4	63 Eu 152.0	64 Gd 157.3	65 Tb 158.9	66 Dy 162.5	67 Ho 164.9	68 Er 167.3	69 Tm 168.9	70 Yb 173.0	71 Lu 175.0
†Actinide Series:	90 Th 232.0	91 Pa (231)	92 U 238.0	93 Np (237)	94 Pu (244)	95 Am (243)	96 Cm (247)	97 Bk (247)	98 Cf (251)	99 Es (252)	100 Fm (257)	101 Md (258)	102 No (259)	103 Lr (260)

4.6

The periodic table can be divided into blocks, as shown above. The name of the block (*s*, *p*, *d*, or *f*) indicates the highest-energy subshell containing electrons in the ground-state of an atom within that block. For example, carbon is in the *p* block, and its electron configuration is $1s^2 2s^2 2p^2$; the highest-energy subshell that contains electrons (the $2p$) is a *p* subshell. In addition, each horizontal row in the periodic table is called a **period**, and each vertical column is called a **group** (or **family**). The bold numbers next to the rows on the left indicate the period number; for example, potassium (K, atomic number 19) is in Period 4.

How do we use this block diagram to write electron configurations? To illustrate, let's say we want to write the configuration for chlorine ($Z = 17$). To get to $Z = 17$, imagine starting at $Z = 1$ (hydrogen) and filling up the subshells as we move along through the rows to $Z = 17$. (Notice that helium has been moved over next to hydrogen for purposes of this block diagram.) We'll first have $1s^2$ for the 2 atoms in Period 1, *s* block ($Z = 1$ and $Z = 2$); the $2s^2$ for the next 2 atoms, which are in Period 2, *s* block ($Z = 3$ and $Z = 4$); then $2p^6$ for the next 6 atoms, which are in Period 2, *p* block ($Z = 5$ through $Z = 10$); the $3s^2$ for the next 2 atoms, which are in Period 3, *s* block ($Z = 11$ and $Z = 12$); then, finally, $3p^5$ for the atoms starting with aluminum, Al, in Period 3, *p* block and counting through to chlorine, Cl. So, we've gone through the rows and blocks from the beginning and stopped once we hit the atom we wanted, and along the way we obtained $1s^2 2s^2 2p^6 3s^2 3p^5$. This is the electron configuration of chlorine.

The noble gases are often used as starting points, because they are at the end of the rows and represent a shell being completely filled; all that's left is to count over in the next row until the desired atom is reached. We find the closest noble gas that has an atomic number less than that of the atom for which we want to find an electron configuration. In the case of chlorine ($Z = 17$), the closest noble gas with a smaller atomic number is neon ($Z = 10$). Starting with neon, we have 7 additional electrons to take care of. To get to $Z = 17$, we go through the 2 atoms in the *s* block of Period 3 ($3s^2$), then notice that Cl is the fifth element in the *p* block, giving us $3p^5$. Therefore, the electron configuration of chlorine is the same as that of neon plus $3s^2 3p^5$, which we can write like this: Cl = [Ne] $3s^2 3p^5$.

The simple counting through the rows and blocks works as long as you remember this simple rule: Whenever you're in the *d* block, *subtract 1 from the period number.* For example, the first row of the *d* block ($Z = 21$ through $Z = 30$) is in Period 4, but instead of saying that these elements have their outermost (or **valence**) electrons in the 4*d* subshell, we subtract 1 from the period number and say that these elements put their valence electrons in the 3*d* subshell.

In summary: The block in the table tells us in which subshell the outermost (valence) electrons of the atom will be. The period (row) gives the shell, *n*, as long as we remember the following fact about the atoms in the *d* block: electrons for an atom in the *d* block of Period *n* go into the subshell $(n–1)d$. For example, the electron configuration for scandium (Sc, atomic number 21) is $[Ar]4s^23d^1$. (Note: if you ever need to write the electron configuration for an element in the *f* block, the rule is: *In the f block, subtract 2 from the period number.*)

Example 4-21: Which of the following gives the electron configuration of an aluminum atom?

A) $1s^22s^22p^1$
B) $1s^22s^22p^2$
C) $1s^22s^22p^63s^23p^1$
D) $1s^22s^22p^63s^23p^2$

Solution: Since aluminum (Al) has atomic number 13, a neutral aluminum atom must have 13 electrons. This observation alone eliminates choices A, B, and D (which indicate a total of 5, 6, and 14 electrons, respectively), so the answer must be C.

Example 4-22: What is the maximum number of electrons that can be present in the $n = 3$ shell?

A) 6
B) 9
C) 12
D) 18

Solution: Every new energy level (*n*) adds a new subshell. That means that in the first energy level we have only the *s* subshell, while when $n = 2$ we have both *s* and *p* subshells, and when $n = 3$, there are *s*, *p*, and *d* subshells. Since there are 1, 3, and 5 *s*, *p*, and *d* orbitals, respectively, for a total of 9 orbitals, and since the maximum number of electrons in an orbital is 2, there can be a maximum of 18 electrons in the $n = 3$ shell.

Example 4-23: What's the electron configuration of a zirconium atom ($Z = 40$)?

A) $[Kr]\ 4d^4$
B) $[Kr]\ 5s^24d^2$
C) $[Kr]\ 5s^25p^2$
D) $[Kr]\ 5s^25d^2$

Solution: Zirconium (Zr) is in the *d* block of Period 5. After krypton (Kr, atomic number 36), we'll have $5s^2$ for the next 2 atoms in the Period 5, *s* block ($Z = 37$ and $Z = 38$). Then, remembering the rule that electrons for an atom in the *d* block of Period *n* go into the subshell $(n – 1)d$, we know that the last two electrons will go in the 4*d* (not the 5*d*) subshell. Therefore, the answer is B.

Some Anomalous Electron Configurations

The process described above (reading across the periodic table, from top to bottom and left to right, using the blocks as a tool for the order of filling of subshells) to determine an atom's electron configuration works quite well for a large percentage of the elements, but there are a few atoms for which the anticipated electron configuration is not the actual configuration observed.

In a few instances, atoms can achieve a lower energy state (or a higher degree of stability) *by having a filled or half-filled, d subshell.* For example, consider chromium (Cr, Z = 24). On the basis of the block diagram, we'd expect its electron configuration to be [Ar] $4s^2 3d^4$. Recalling that a d subshell can hold a maximum of 10 electrons, it turns out that chromium achieves a more stable state by filling its d subshell with 5 electrons (*half-filled*) rather than leaving it with 4. This is accomplished by promoting one of its $4s$ electrons to the $3d$ subshell, yielding the electron configuration [Ar]$4s^1 3d^5$. As another example, copper (Cu, Z = 29) has an expected electron configuration of [Ar] $4s^2 3d^9$. However, a copper atom obtains a more stable, lower-energy state by promoting one of its $4s$ electrons into the $3d$ subshell, yielding [Ar] $4s^1 3d^{10}$ to give a *filled d* subshell.

Other atoms that display the same type of behavior with regard to their electron configuration as do chromium and copper include molybdenum (Mo, $Z = 42$, in the same family as chromium), as well as silver and gold (Ag and Au, $Z = 47$ and $Z = 79$, respectively, which are in the same family as copper).

Example 4-24: What is the electron configuration of an atom of silver?

Solution: As mentioned above, silver is one of the handful of elements with atoms that actually achieve greater overall stability by promoting one of its electrons into a higher subshell in order to make it filled. We'd expect the electron configuration for silver to be [Kr]$5s^2 4d^9$. But, by analogy with copper, we'd predict (correctly) that the actual configuration of silver is [Kr] $5s^1 4d^{10}$, where the atom obtains a more stable state by promoting one of its $5s$ electrons into the $4d$ subshell, to give a *filled d* subshell.

Electron Configurations of Ions

Recall that an ion is an atom that has acquired a nonzero electric charge. An atom with more electrons than protons is negatively charged and is called an anion; an atom with fewer electrons than protons is positively charged and is called a cation.

Atoms that gain electrons (anions) accommodate them in the first available orbital, the one with the lowest available energy. For example, fluorine (F, Z = 9) has the electron configuration $1s^2 2s^2 2p^5$. When a fluorine atom gains an electron to become the fluoride ion, F^-, the additional electron goes into the $2p$ subshell, giving the electron configuration $1s^2 2s^2 2p^6$, which is the same as the configuration of neon. For this reason, F^- and Ne are said to be **isoelectronic**.

In order to write the electron configuration of an ion for an element in the s or p blocks, we can use the blocks in the periodic table as follows. If an atom becomes an anion—that is, if it acquires one or more additional electrons—then we move to the *right* within the table by a number of squares equal to the number of electrons added in order to find the atom with the same configuration as the ion.

If an atom becomes a cation—that is, if it loses one or more electrons—then we move to the *left* within the table by a number of squares equal to the number of electrons lost in order to find the atom with the same configuration as the ion.

Example 4-25: What's the electron configuration of P^{3-}? Of Sr^+?

Solution: To find the configuration of P^{3-}, we locate phosphorus (P, $Z = 15$) in the periodic table and move 3 places to the *right* (because we have an anion with charge of 3^-); this lands us on argon (Ar, $Z = 18$). Therefore, the electron configuration of the anion P^{3-} is the same as that of argon: $1s^22s^22p^63s^23p^6$.

To find the configuration of Sr^+, we locate strontium (Sr, $Z = 38$) in the periodic table and move 1 place to the *left* (because we have a cation with charge 1+), thus landing on rubidium (Rb, $Z = 37$). Therefore, the electron configuration of the anion Sr^+ is the same as that of rubidium: [Kr] $5s^1$.

Electrons that are removed *(ionized)* from an atom always come from the valence shell (the highest n level), and the highest energy orbital within that level. For example, an atom of lithium, Li ($1s^22s^1$), becomes Li^+ ($1s^2$) when it absorbs enough energy for an electron to escape. However, recall from our discussion above that **transition metals** (which are the elements in the d block) have both ns and $(n - 1)d$ electrons. To form a cation, atoms will always lose their valence electrons first, and since $n > n - 1$, transition metals lose s electrons *before* they lose d electrons. Only after *all s* electrons are lost do d electrons get ionized. For example, the electron configuration for the transition metal titanium (Ti, $Z = 22$) is [Ar] $4s^23d^2$. We might expect that the electron configuration of the ion Ti^+ to be [Ar] $4s^23d^1$ since the d electrons are slightly higher in energy. However, the *actual* configuration is [Ar] $4s^13d^2$, and the valence electrons (the ones from the highest n level) are ALWAYS lost first. Similarly, the electron configuration of Ti^{2+} is not [Ar] $4s^2$—it's actually [Ar] $3d^2$.

Example 4-26: Which one of the following ions has the same electron configuration as the noble gas argon?

A) Na^+
B) P^{2-}
C) Al^{3+}
D) Cl^-

Solution: Na^+ (choice A) has the same electron configuration as the noble gas *neon*, not argon, since one element to the left of Na is Ne. The ion P^{2-} has the same electron configuration as Cl, which is two elements to the right of P. Al^{3+}, like Na^+, has the same configuration as Ne. Of the choices given, only Cl^- (choice D) has the same configuration as Ar, since Ar is one element to the right of Cl.

Example 4-27: What's the electron configuration of Cu^+? Of Cu^{2+}? Of Fe^{3+}?

Solution: Copper (Cu, $Z = 29$) is a transition metal, so it will lose its valence s electrons before losing any d electrons. Recall the anomalous electron configuration of Cu (to give it a filled $3d$ subshell): [Ar] $4s^13d^{10}$. Therefore, the configuration of Cu^+ (the *cuprous* ion, Cu(I)) is [Ar] $3d^{10}$, and that of Cu^{2+} (the *cupric* ion, Cu(II)) is [Ar] $3d^9$. Since the electron configuration of iron (Fe, $Z = 26$) is [Ar] $4s^23d^6$, the configuration of Fe^{3+} (the *ferric* ion, Fe(III)) is [Ar] $3d^5$, since the transition metal atom Fe first loses both of its valence s electrons, then once they're ionized, one of its d electrons.

Excited State vs. Ground State

Assigning electron configurations as we've just discussed is aimed at constructing the *most probable* location of electrons, following the Aufbau principle. These configurations are the most probable because they are the lowest in energy, or as they are often termed, the ground state.

Any electron configuration of an atom that is *not* as we would assign it, provided it doesn't break any physical rules (no more than $2e^-$ per orbital, no assigning non existent shells such as $2d$, etc....) is an excited state. The atom has absorbed energy, so the electrons now inhabit states we wouldn't predict as the most probable ones.

Example 4-28: Which of the following could be the electron configuration of an excited oxygen atom?

A) $1s^22s^22p^4$
B) $1s^22s^22p^5$
C) $1s^22s^22p^33s^1$
D) $1s^22s^22p^43s^1$

Solution: An oxygen atom contains 8 electrons; when excited, one (or more) of these electrons will jump to a higher energy level. Choice A is the configuration of a ground-state oxygen atom, and choices B and D show the placement of 9 electrons, not 8, so both may be eliminated. The answer must be C; one of the $2p$ electrons has jumped to the $3s$ subshell. (Note carefully that an excited atom is not an ion; electrons are not lost or gained; they simply jump to higher energy levels within the atom.

4.7 GROUPS OF THE PERIODIC TABLE AND THEIR CHARACTERISTICS

We will use the electron configurations of the atoms to predict their chemical properties, including their reactivity and bonding patterns with other atoms.

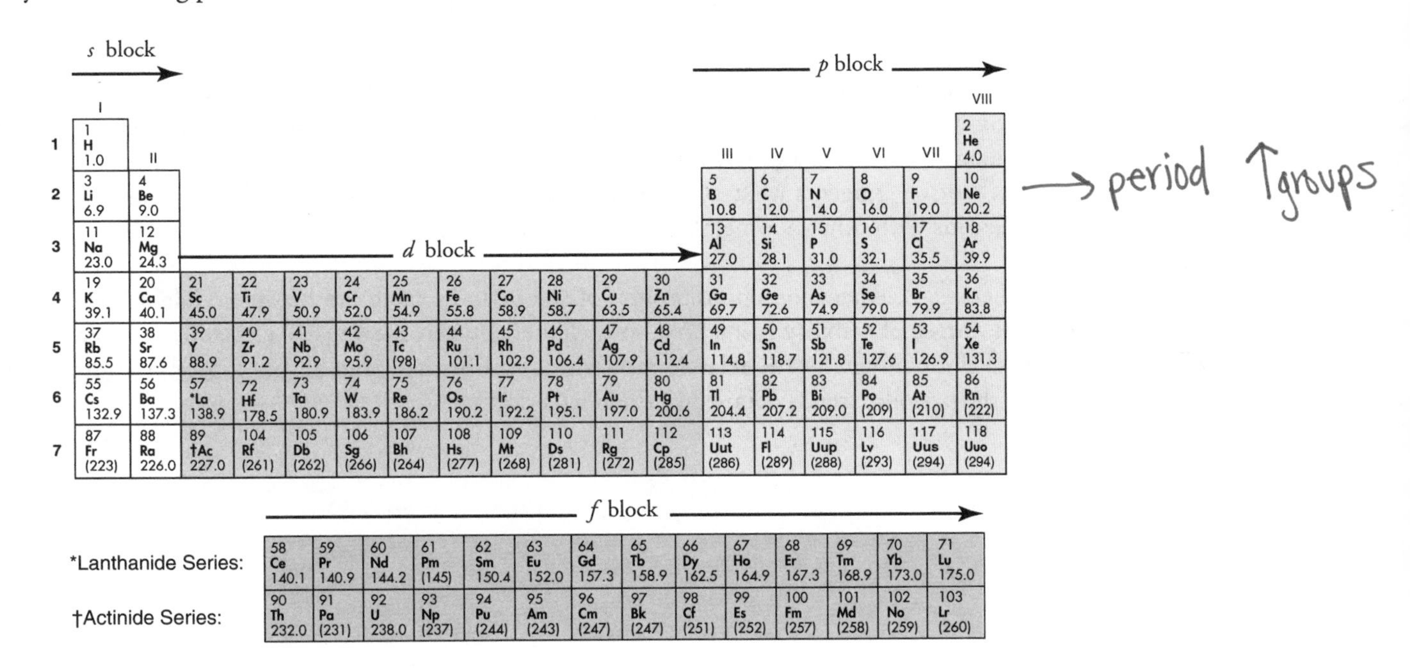

Recall that each horizontal row in the periodic table is called a **period**, and each vertical column is called a **group** (or **family**). Within any group in the periodic table, all of the elements have the same number of electrons in their outermost shell. For instance, the elements in Group II all have two electrons in their outermost shell. Electrons in an atom's outermost shell are called **valence** electrons, and it's the valence electrons that are primarily responsible for an atom's properties and chemical behavior.

Some groups (families) have special names.

Group	Name	Valence-Shell Configuration
Group I	*Alkali metals*	ns^1
Group II	*Alkaline earth metals*	ns^2
Group VII	*Halogens*	ns^2np^5
Group VIII	*Noble gases*	ns^2np^6
The *d* Block	*Transition metals*	
The *s* and *p* Blocks	*Representative elements*	
The *f* Block	*Rare earth metals*	

The valence-shell electron configuration determines the chemical reactivity of each group in the table. For example, in the noble gas family each element has eight electrons in its outermost shell (ns^2np^6). Such a closed-shell (fully-filled valence shell) configuration is called an octet and results in great stability (and therefore low reactivity) for an atom. For this reason, noble gases do not generally undergo chemical reactions, so most group VIII elements are inert. Helium is inert as well, but has a closed shell with a stable duet ($1s^2$) of electrons.

Other elements experience similar increases in stability upon reaching this stable octet electron configuration, and most chemical reactions can be regarded as the quest for atoms to achieve such closed-shell stability. The alkali metals and alkaline earth metals, for instance, possess one (ns^1) or two (ns^2) electrons in their valence shells, respectively, and behave as reducing agents (i.e., lose valence electrons) in redox reactions in order to obtain a stable octet, generally as an M^+ or M^{2+} cation.

Similarly, the halogens (ns^2np^5) require only a single electron to achieve a stable octet. To achieve this state in their elemental form, halogens naturally exist as diatomic molecules (e.g., F_2) where one electron from each atom is shared in a covalent bond. When combined with other elements, the halogens behave as powerful oxidizing agents (that is, gain electrons); they can become stable either as X^- anions or by sharing electrons with other nonmetals (more on bonding in Ch. 5).

Reactions between elements on opposite sides of the periodic table can be quite violent. This occurs due to the great degree of stability gained for both elements when the valence electrons are transferred from the metal to the nonmetal. The relative reactivities within these and all other groups can be further explained by the periodic trends detailed in the next section.

Example 4-29: Which of the following elements has a closed valence shell, but not an octet?

A) He
B) Ne
C) Br
D) Rn

Solution: Choice A, He, is the correct choice because He, along with H^- and Li^+, has a completed $n = 1$ shell with only 2 electrons, since the $n = 1$ shell can fit only 2 electrons.

Example 4-30: Which of the following could describe an ion with the same electron configuration as a noble gas?

A) An alkali metal that has gained an electron
B) A halogen that has lost an electron
C) A transition metal that has gained an electron
D) An alkaline earth metal that has lost two electrons

Solution: Choice A is wrong since it says "gained" rather than "lost." Choice B is incorrect since it says "lost" rather than "gained." Choice C is also incorrect, because no element in the *d* block could acquire a noble-gas configuration by gaining a single electron. The answer must be D. If an element in Group II loses two electrons, it can acquire a noble-gas electron configuration. (For example, Mg^{2+} has the same configuration as Ne, and Ca^{2+} has the same configuration as Ar.)

Example 4-31: Of the following, the element that possesses properties of both metals and nonmetals is:

A) Si
B) Al
C) Zn
D) Hg

Solution: Elements that possess qualities of both metals and nonmetals are called *metalloids*. These elements are shown below. Thus, choice A is the correct answer; the other choices are metals.

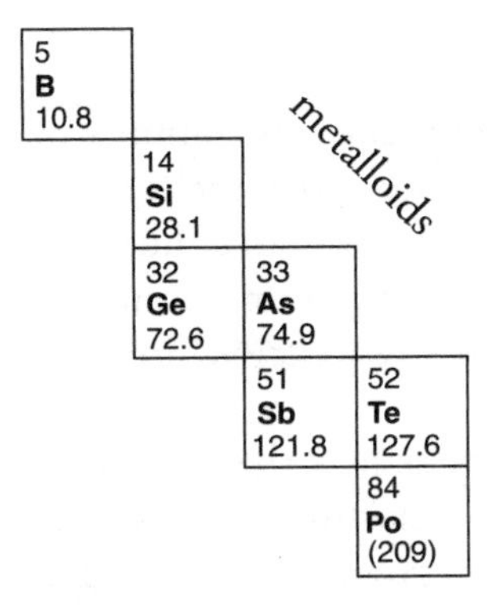

★4.8 PERIODIC TRENDS

Shielding

Each filled shell between the nucleus and the valence electrons shields—or "protects"—the valence electrons from the full effect of the positively charged protons in the nucleus. This is called **nuclear shielding** or the **shielding effect**. As far as the valence electrons are concerned, the electrical pull by the protons in the nucleus is reduced by the negative charges of the electrons in the filled shells in between; the result is an effective reduction in the positive elementary charge, from Z to a smaller amount denoted by Z_{eff} (for *effective nuclear charge*).

4.8

Example 4-32: The electrons in a solitary He atom are under the influence of two forces, one attractive and one repulsive. What are these forces?

A) Electrostatic attraction between the electrons and the nuclear protons, and electrostatic repulsion between the electrons and nuclear neutrons.
B) Electrostatic attraction between the electrons and the nuclear protons, and electrostatic repulsion between the electrons.
C) Gravitational attraction between the electrons and the nuclear protons, and frictional repulsion between the electrons.
D) Gravitational attraction between the electrons and the entire nucleus, and frictional repulsion between the electrons.

Solution: Compared to the magnitude of electrostatic forces in an atom, gravitational forces between the electrons and nucleons of an atom are negligible, so choices C and D are eliminated. Furthermore, neutrons have no charge and thus do not participate in electrostatic forces, so choice A is eliminated. Remember that opposite charges attract and like charges repel. The best choice is B.

Atomic and Ionic Radius

With progression across any period in the table, the number of protons increases, and hence their total pull on the outermost electrons increases, too. New shells are initiated only at the beginning of a period. So, as we go across a period, electrons are being added, but new shells are not; therefore, the valence electrons are more and more tightly bound to the atom because they feel a greater effective nuclear charge. Therefore, as we move from left to right across a period, **atomic radius** *decreases*.

However, with progression down a group, as new shells are added with each period, the valence electrons experience increased shielding. The valence electrons are less tightly bound since they feel a smaller effective nuclear charge. Therefore, as we go down a group, atomic radius *increases* due to the increased shielding.

If we form an ion, the radius will decrease as electrons are removed (because the ones that are left are drawn in more closely to the nucleus), and the radius will increase as electrons are added. So, in terms of radius, we have $X^+ < X < X^-$; that is, cation radius < neutral-atom radius < anion radius.

Ionization Energy

Because the atom's positively charged nucleus is attracted to the electrons in the atom, it takes energy to remove an electron. The amount of energy necessary to remove the least tightly bound electron from an isolated atom is called the atom's **(first) ionization energy** (often abbreviated **IE** or **IE_1**). As we move from left to right across a period, or up a group, the ionization energy *increases* since the valence electrons are more tightly bound. The ionization energy of any atom with a noble-gas configuration will always be very large. (For example, the ionization energy of neon is 4 times greater than that of lithium.) The **second ionization energy** (**IE_2**) of an atom, X, is the energy required to remove the least tightly bound electron from the cation X^+. Note that IE_2 will always be greater than IE_1.

Electron Affinity

The energy associated with the addition of an electron to an isolated atom is known as the atom's **electron affinity** (often abbreviated **EA**). If energy is *released* when the electron is added, the usual convention is to say that the electron affinity is negative; if energy is *required* in order to add the electron, the electron affinity is positive. The halogens have large negative electron affinity values, since the addition of an electron would give them the much desired octet configuration. So they readily accept an electron to become an anion; the increase in stability causes energy to be released. On the other hand, the noble gases and alkaline earth metals have positive electron affinities, because the added electron begins to fill a new level or sublevel and destabilizes the electron configuration. Therefore, anions of these atoms are unstable. Electron affinities typically become more negative as we move to the right across a row or up a group (noble gases excepted), but there are anomalies in this trend.

Electronegativity

Electronegativity is a measure of an atom's ability to pull electrons to itself when it forms a covalent bond; the greater this tendency to attract electrons, the greater the atom's electronegativity. Electronegativity generally behaves as does ionization energy; that is, as we move from left to right across a period, electronegativity increases. As we go down a group, electronegativity decreases. You should know the order of electronegativity for the nine most electronegative elements:

$$F > O > N \approx Cl > Br > I > S > C \approx H$$

Acidity

Acidity is a measure of how well a compound donates protons, accepts electrons, or lowers pH in a chemical system. A binary acid has the structure HX, and can dissociate in water in the following manner: $HX \rightarrow H^+ + X^-$. Stronger acids have resulting X^- anions that are likely to separate from H^+ because they are stable once they do. Generally speaking, the ease with which an acid (HX) donates its H^+ is directly related to the stability of the conjugate base (X^-). With respect to the *horizontal* periodic trend for acidity, the more electronegative the element bearing the negative charge is, the more stable the anion will be. Therefore acidity increases from left to right across a period. However, the *vertical* trend for acidity depends on the size of the anion. The larger the anion, the more the negative charge can be delocalized and stabilized. Therefore, acidity increases down a group or family in the periodic table.

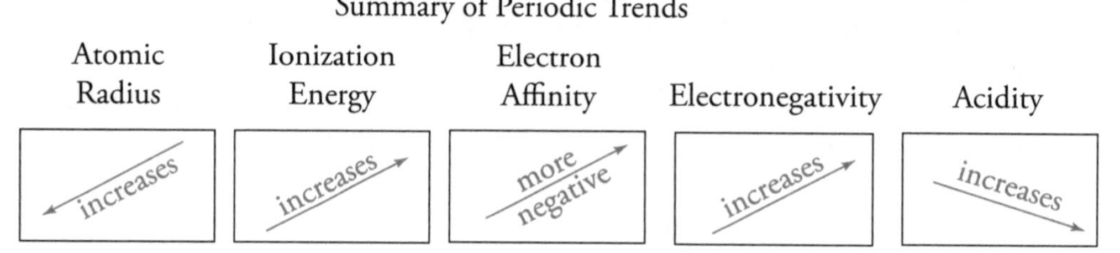

4.8

Example 4-33: Compared to calcium, beryllium is expected to have:

A) greater electronegativity and ionization energy.
B) smaller electronegativity and ionization energy.
C) greater electronegativity and smaller ionization energy.
D) smaller electronegativity and larger ionization energy

Solution: Beryllium and calcium are in the same group, but beryllium is higher in the column. We therefore expect beryllium to have greater ionization energy and a greater electronegativity than calcium (choice A), since both of these periodic trends tend to increase as we go up within a group.

Example 4-34: Which of the following will have a greater value for phosphorus than for magnesium?

I. Atomic radius
II. Ionization energy
III. Electronegativity

A) I only
B) I and II only
C) II and III only
D) I, II, and III

Solution: Magnesium and phosphorus are in the same period (row), but phosphorus is farther to the right. We therefore expect phosphorus to have a smaller atomic radius, making Roman numeral I false. This allows us to eliminate choices A, B, and D, leaving C as the correct answer. This is also consistent as we expect phosphorus to have a greater ionization energy and a greater electronegativity than magnesium, since both of these periodic trends tend to increase as we move to the right across a row. However, we expect the atomic radius of phosphorus to be smaller than that of magnesium, since atomic radii tend to *decrease* as we move to the right across a row. Therefore, the answer is C.

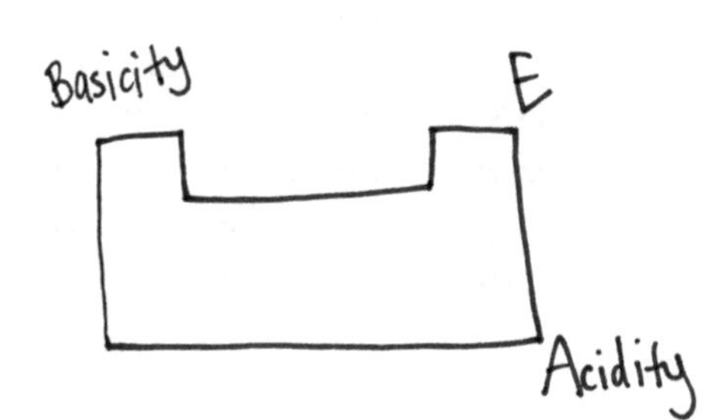

Example: 4-35 Of the following, which has the most negative electron affinity?

A) Barium
B) Bromine
C) Phosphorus
D) Chlorine

Solution: Barium is in Group II and therefore has a large positive electron affinity, so we can eliminate choice A immediately. Because electron affinity values tend to become more negative as we go to the right across a row or up within a column, we'd expect chlorine to have a more negative electron affinity than phosphorus or bromine. Therefore, choice D is the answer.

Example 4-36: Of the following, which has the smallest atomic radius?

A) Sodium
B) Oxygen
C) Calcium
D) Silicon

Solution: The atoms with the *smallest* atomic radius are those in the *upper right* portion of the periodic table, since atomic radius tends to increase as we move to the left or down a column. We can therefore eliminate choices A and C; these elements are in Groups I and II, respectively, at the far left end of the table. To decide between the remaining choices, we notice that oxygen is farther to the right *and* in a higher row than silicon, so we'd expect an oxygen atom to have a smaller radius than a silicon atom. Choice B is the best answer.

Example 4-37: Of the following, which is the strongest acid?

A) H_2O
B) H_2S
C) HCl
D) HBr

Solution: For binary acids, we expect acidity to increase with increasing stability of the conjugate base. When comparing anions in a period, those that are more electronegative are more stable. Since chloride is more electronegative than sulfide, choice B can be eliminated. In addition, when comparing anions in a family, those that are larger are more stable, so choices A and C can also be eliminated, making choice D the best answer.

Chapter 4 Summary

- The nucleus contains protons and neutrons. Their sum corresponds to the mass number (A).
- The number of protons corresponds to the atomic number (Z).
- An overabundance of either protons or neutrons can result in unstable nuclei, which decay via the emission of various particles.
- For nuclear decay reactions, the sum of all mass and atomic numbers in the products must equal the same sum of these numbers in the reactants.
- The rate of nuclear decay is governed by a species' half-life.
- Electrons exist in discrete energy levels within an atom. Emission spectra are obtained from energy emitted as excited electrons fall from one level to another.
- The periodic table is organized into blocks based on the architecture of electron orbitals. Therefore, valence electron configurations can be determined based on an element's location in the table.
- In their ground state, electrons occupy the lowest energy orbitals available, and occupy subshell orbitals singly before pairing.
- Atoms and ions are most stable when they have an octet of electrons in their outer shell.
- The *d* subshell is always backfilled: for an atom in the *d* block of period n, the *d* subshell will have a principle quantum number of $n - 1$.
- A half filled (d^5) or filled (d^{10}) *d* subshell is exceptionally stable.
- Transition metals ionize from their valence *s* subshell before their *d* subshell.
- Atomic radius increases to the left and down the periodic table; for charged species, cations $<$ neutral atom $<$ anions for a given element; for isoelectronic ions, the species with more protons will have the smaller radius.
- Ionization energy, electron affinity, and electronegativity increase up and to the right on the periodic table, while acidity increases to the right and down the periodic table.
- The relative electronegativities of common atoms in decreasing order are F O N Cl Br I S C $\approx$ H.

CHAPTER 4 FREESTANDING PRACTICE QUESTIONS

1. When an atom of plutonium-239 is bombarded with an alpha particle, this element along with one free neutron is created:

A) Californium-240
B) Californium-241
C) Curium-242
D) Curium-243

2. Which of the following represents the correct ground state electronic configuration for ferrous ion, Fe^{2+}?

A) [Ar] $4s^23d^6$
B) [Ar] $4s^23d^4$
C) [Ar] $3d^6$
D) [Ar] $4s^23d^2$

3. Which atom has three unpaired electrons in its valence energy level?

A) Li
B) Be
C) C
D) N

4. Which of the following elements would be most strongly attracted to a magnetic field?

A) Mg
B) Ca
C) Cr
D) Zn

5. Which of the following colors would appear as a bright band in an emission spectrum of a yellow sodium vapor lamp?

A) Yellow, indicating a lesser wavelength than ultraviolet light
B) Yellow, indicating a greater wavelength than ultraviolet light
C) Blue, indicating a lesser wavelength than ultraviolet light
D) Blue, indicating a greater wavelength than ultraviolet light

6. Which of the following atoms/ions has electrons in the subshell of highest energy?

A) Cl^-
B) Ca^{2+}
C) Cr^+
D) As

7. Of the following metallic elements, which has the lowest second ionization energy?

A) Na
B) K
C) Mg
D) Ca

8. Which of the following has the smallest atomic or ionic radius?

A) Cl^-
B) Ar
C) K^+
D) Ca^{2+}

9. Metallic character results from an element's ability to lose electrons. On the periodic table it is expected that metallic character increases:

A) from left to right, because the decrease in electronegativity would make it easier to lose electrons.
B) from left to right, because the decrease in atomic radius would result in more stable positive ions.
C) from right to left, because the decrease in ionization energy would make it easier to lose electrons.
D) from right to left, because the decrease in electron affinity would result in more stable positive ions.

CHAPTER 4 PRACTICE PASSAGE

The term "first ionization energy" is the minimum amount of energy that an atom in the gaseous state must absorb to release its outermost electron, thereby creating an ion with a charge of +1. The "second ionization energy" is the amount of energy necessary to cause the removal of the second outermost electron (after the first electron has already been removed), thereby creating an ion with a charge of +2. If an atom loses enough electrons to leave the resulting ion with a "stable octet" noble-gas electron configuration, the energy necessary to remove yet another electron will greatly exceed that which was needed to remove any of the previously displaced electrons.

A series of experiments is conducted involving the apparatus shown in Figure 1. It consists of an evacuated glass tube with an electrode situated at each end. Intake and exhaust valves are located along the upper surface of the tube so that gas may be introduced into the tube and removed.

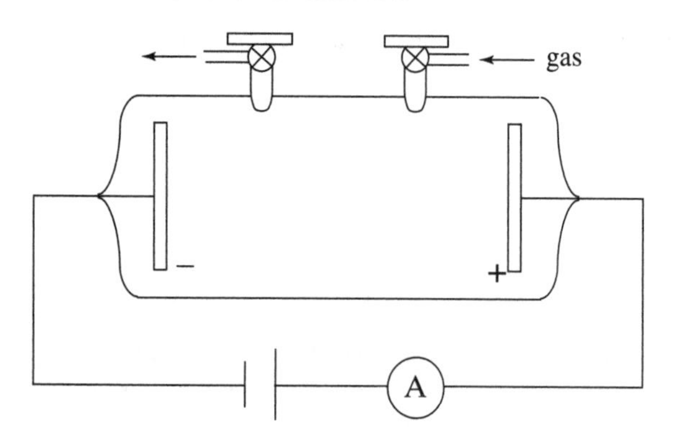

Figure 1

For each experiment, an *elemental* gas is introduced via the intake valve. While the gas remains in the glass tube the potential difference (voltage) across the electrode plates is gradually increased. As the voltage increases, it ultimately reaches a level high enough to provide the gas atoms with energy equal to their first ionization energy. In such an experimental situation the voltage that corresponds to the first ionization energy is termed the "ionization potential." When the voltage is raised to a level equal to the ionization potential, gas ions are formed and a sudden surge of current flow within the tube is noted and recorded.

For a variety of properties, including electron affinity and ionization energy, the elements follow well established periodic trends. For any given element these trends are significant to chemical behavior and reactivity. Table 1 records measured ionization energies for several elements.

Element	First Ionization Energy (eV/atom)	Second Ionization Energy (eV/atom)
Hydrogen	13.6	
Helium	24.6	
Lithium	5.4	
Nitrogen	14.5	
Neon	21.6	
Sodium	5.1	
Magnesium	7.6	
Titanium	6.8	13.6
Iron	7.9	16

Table 1

1. Which of the following represent the likely values of the first ionization energies of K and Cs (in eV), respectively?

A) K = 5.2; Cs = 4.3
B) K = 4.3; Cs = 5.2
C) K = 4.3; Cs = 3.8
D) K = 3.8; Cs = 4.3

2. Although the second ionization energies for Na and Mg do not appear in Table 1, it is most likely that the second ionization energy of Na will be:

A) less than that of Mg, because its first ionization energy is also less.
B) less than that of Mg, because Na^+ has a smaller effective nuclear charge than Mg^+.
C) greater than that of Mg, because Na^{2+} is more stable than Mg^{2+}.
D) greater than that of Mg, because the valence electron of Na^+ is in a 2*p* orbital, whereas that of Mg^+ is in a 3*s* orbital.

3. The voltage in the tube is adjusted to provide the circulating gas atoms with energy equal to 10 eV. Which of the following species can undergo ionization?

A) H, He, and Li
B) H, He, and N
C) Mg, Ti, and Fe^{+}
D) Na, Mg, and Ti

4. Without information like that provided in Table 1, the experimental device shown in Figure 1 would fail to aid a researcher in identifying a tested elemental gas because the researcher would lack which of the following?

A) A control against which to compare the electrochemical events within the glass tube and the hypotheses on which the experiment is based
B) A rational basis on which to draw conclusions because the electrochemical event could not be associated with the phenomenon of ionization
C) A reference standard from which to draw conclusions based on the voltage magnitude at which the apparatus experiences a current surge
D) A scientifically designed experimental model since any appropriately controlled study requires a pre-existing data base as its premise

5. When the same setup was used to measure gaseous H_2 and N_2, ionization energies of 15.6 and 15.5 eV, respectively, were recorded. Which of the following correctly rationalizes the discrepancy between these values and the energies found for the elemental gases?

A) The electrons in the σ and π bonds of H_2 and N_2 are diffuse about the molecular surface, and hence more weakly held than in the elemental gases.
B) Nitrogen is more stable in its –3 oxidation state, and hydrogen in its +1 oxidation state, than in their neutral atomic states.
C) Bonding arrangements necessarily increase the stability of the electrons involved in any atom.
D) Large dipoles in molecules act to increase the ionization energy of electrons constituting the molecule.

SOLUTIONS TO CHAPTER 4 FREESTANDING PRACTICE QUESTIONS

1. C The process described is transmutation, and the new nucleus can be determined by writing a balanced nuclear equation. The preliminary equation to balance is this:

$$^{239}_{94}\text{Pu} + {}^{4}_{2}\alpha \rightarrow {}^{1}_{0}\text{n} + {}^{A}_{Z}?$$

where the question mark stands for the new element formed. Balancing mass number gives $239 + 4 = 1 + A$, where $A = 242$; balancing the atomic number gives $94 + 2 = 0 + Z$, where $Z = 96$. Therefore, element number 96 is curium (eliminate choices A and B), and the appropriate isotope has a mass number of 242.

2. C When answering electron configuration questions, the first step is to eliminate all answer choices that do not display the correct number of electrons. In this case, ferrous ion possesses six electrons beyond those represented by [Ar] (eight for elemental iron minus two to generate the +2 cation). Thus, choices A and D can be eliminated. To choose between B and C, recall that when transition metals ionize, it is the outermost and therefore least tightly held electrons that are removed first. In this case, the 4*s* electrons are further from the nucleus and are less tightly held ($n = 4$ represents a greater radial distance from the nucleus than $n = 3$). Thus they are the first to be removed.

3. D Since Li has only one valence electron and Be has only two, neither choices A nor B can be correct. To choose between C and D, note that the valence configuration of C is $2s^2 2p^2$. Thus the 2*s* electrons are paired leaving only two unpaired *p* electrons. Nitrogen has a valence configuration of $2s^2 2p^3$, and by Hund's rule, the three *p* electrons will singly occupy the p_x, p_y, and p_z levels rather than pairing up to avoid electron repulsion.

4. C Diamagnetic atoms are repelled by magnetic fields and paramagnetic atoms are attracted to magnetic fields. Paramagnetic atoms have unpaired electrons in their valence orbitals. Mg and Ca are in the same group and have the same valence configuration, so both cannot be the right answer. Zn is at the end of the *d* block and has a valence shell with all of its electrons paired. Cr only has five electrons in its 3*d* subshell, resulting in five unpaired electron orbitals. Cr is the only choice that is paramagnetic and would be attracted to a magnetic field.

5. B All visible light has a greater wavelength than ultraviolet, eliminating choices A and C. The sodium lamp glows yellow and would therefore emit a yellow band on a dark background. If the question asked where dark bands would have been in an absorption spectrum, several lines would be seen in regions other than yellow since those colors are absorbed.

6. D Electron energy level is determined by the first two quantum numbers. Given Cl^- = [Kr], Ca^{2+} = [Ar], Cr^+ = [Ar] $3d^5$, and As = [Ar] $4s^2 3d^{10} 4p^3$, arsenic contains electrons in the highest energy subshell, 4*p*.

7. D After their first ionizations, Na^+ and K^+ both have octet electron configurations, so a second ionization to remove another electron would require a very high amount of energy. This eliminates choices A and B. Ionization energy decreases down a group, due to increased nuclear shielding, so it is easier to remove electrons from Ca than Mg, making choice D the answer.

8. D All four answer choices have the same number of electrons and the same electron configuration. Ca^{2+} has the most protons pulling on these electrons, so it will be the smallest.

9. C Choice A is eliminated because electronegativity increases from left to right on the periodic table. Choice B is eliminated because the stability of positive ions increases as you go up and to the left on the periodic table. Finally, choice D is eliminated since electron affinity is the energy released upon gaining an electron and does not relate to the stability of a positive ion. Choice C is the correct answer because ionization energy, or the energy required to remove an electron, decreases from right to left due to a decrease in effective nuclear charge.

SOLUTIONS TO CHAPTER 4 PRACTICE PASSAGE

1. C As shown in Table 1, the trend in ionization energy within group I is decreasing from H (13.6 eV) at the top to Na (5.1 eV) at the bottom and Li in the middle, with an intermediate value of 5.4 eV. Potassium follows in this sequence after Na and Cs is two more rows down. Therefore, no ionization energies for these two elements should be any higher than 5.1 eV, eliminating choices A and B. Choice D shows Cs as having a greater ionization energy than K, which is the reverse of the observed trend, so can be eliminated.

2. D It will require much more energy to remove an electron from Na^+ than from Mg^+, since Na^+ has a noble-gas configuration, while Mg^+ does not.

3. D Those species with an ionization energy less than 10 eV/atom can be ionized. According to Table 1, hydrogen has an ionization energy of 13.6 eV, so choices A and B are eliminated, and Fe^+ has an ionization energy of 16 eV, so choice C is eliminated.

4. C Table 1 affords the researcher the opportunity to compare data collected to previously measured, known gases. Only with such reference data can the researcher identify an unknown elemental gas. Choices A, B, and D have nothing to do with the identification of an unknown sample by comparing its properties to those of known samples.

5. C The greater stability (higher ionization potential) of the diatomic gases as compared to the elemental gases may be explained by the use of the most energetic electrons in the molecular gas to form bonds, thereby stabilizing them in the molecule. If the formation of bonds did not increase the electronic stability of the molecule, they would not form. A bonding arrangement that is higher in energy than its constitutive atoms would simply fly apart, decreasing the energy of the system. This is what choice C postulates. Choice A may be eliminated as it supposes that the electrons in the elemental gases are more stable than in the diatomic forms of the element, which is inconsistent with the data in Table 1. Choice B is irrelevant, as the oxidation state of H and N in their diatomic forms is still 0, and hence the same as in the elemental gases. Choice D may be eliminated as neither H_2 nor N_2 have a dipole moment.

Chapter 5
Bonding and Intermolecular Forces

The physical properties of a substance are determined at the molecular level, and the chemistry of molecules is dominated by the reactivity of covalent and ionic bonds. An understanding of the fundamentals of bonding can provide the intuitive grasp necessary to answer a wide range of questions in both general and organic chemistry. This chapter will briefly outline some basic principles, that when mastered, will help lay a strong foundation for many chemistry concepts you will encounter on the MCAT.

5.1 LEWIS DOT STRUCTURES

Each dot in the picture below represents one of fluorine's valence electrons. Fluorine is a halogen, with a general valence-shell configuration of ns^2np^5, so there are 2 + 5 = 7 electrons in its valence shell. We simply place the dots around the symbol for the element, one on each side, and, if there are more than 4 valence electrons, we just start pairing them up. So, for fluorine, we'd have:

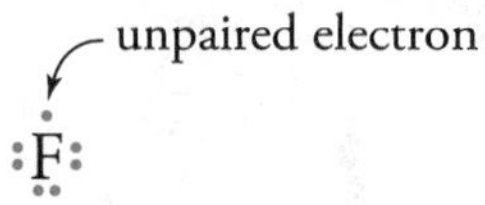

unpaired electron

:F:

This is known as a **Lewis dot symbol**. Here are some others:

K· ·Mg· ·B· ·Si· :P· :O: :Cl: :Ne:

(*Note*: Electrons in *d* subshells are not considered valence electrons for transition metals since valence electrons are in the highest *n* level.)

Example 5-1: Consider this Lewis dot symbol:

·X·

Among the following, X could represent:

A) carbon.
B) nitrogen.
C) sulfur.
D) argon.

Solution: Since there are four dots in the Lewis symbol, X will be an element in Group 4 of the periodic table. Of the choices given, only carbon (choice A) is in Group 4.

Lewis dot structures are one type of model we use to represent what compounds look like at the molecular level. Since it's the valence electrons that are responsible for creating bonds in molecules, a Lewis dot structure that accounts for the number and location of all valence electrons gives us a sense of how molecules are held together and helps us understand their reactivity.

To create a Lewis dot structure for a molecule, we begin to pair up electrons from two separate atoms since two electrons are required to form a single bond. By sharing a pair of electrons to form a bond, each atom may acquire an octet configuration, thereby stabilizing both atoms. For example, each of the fluorine atoms below can donate its unpaired valence electron to form a bond and give the molecule F_2. The shared electrons are attracted by the nuclei of *both* atoms in the bond, which hold the atoms together.

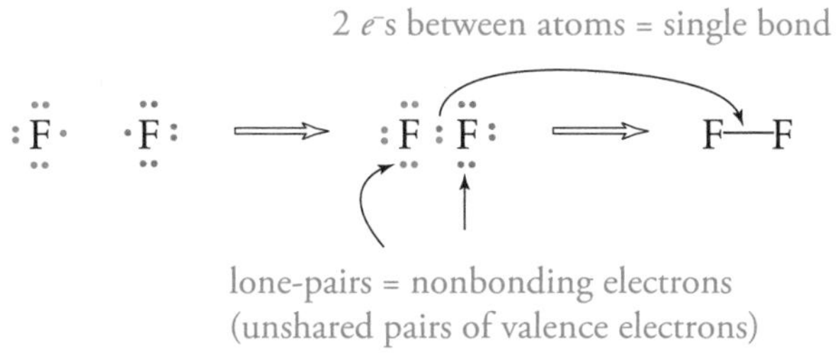

2 e^-s between atoms = single bond

:F· ·F: ⟹ :F:F: ⟹ F—F

lone-pairs = nonbonding electrons
(unshared pairs of valence electrons)

Note that in addition to the **single bond** (a bond formed from two electrons) between the fluorine atoms, each fluorine atom has three pairs of electrons that are not part of a bond. They help satisfy the octets of the F atoms and are known as "lone pairs" of electrons. We'll see in a bit how these lone pairs are important for determining physical properties of compounds, so don't forget to write these out too.

We can also use Lewis dot structures to show atoms that form multiple bonds—**double bonds** use four electrons while **triple bonds** require six. Here are a couple of examples:

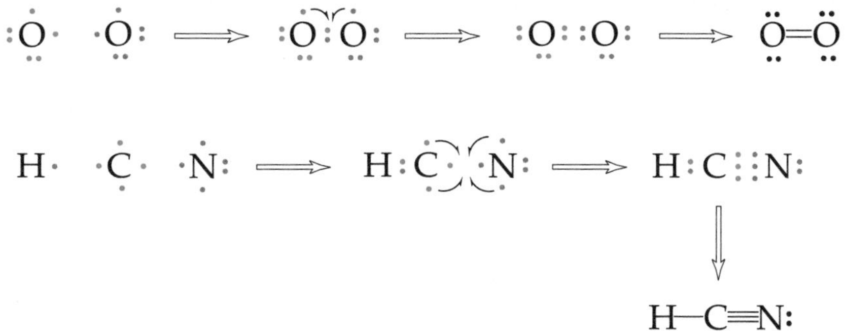

:O· ·O: ⟹ :O:O: ⟹ :O::O: ⟹ O=O

H· ·C· ·N: ⟹ H:C· ·N: ⟹ H:C:::N:

⟹ H—C≡N:

Formal Charge

The last Lewis dot structure shown above for the molecule consisting of 1 atom each of hydrogen, carbon, and nitrogen was drawn with C as the central atom. However, it could have been drawn with N as the central atom, and we could have still achieved closed-shell configurations for all the atoms:

H· ·N: ·C· ⟹ H:N:::C: ⟹ H—N≡C: (?)

The problem is this doesn't give the correct structure for this molecule. The nitrogen atom is not actually bonded to the hydrogen. A helpful way to evaluate a proposed Lewis structure is to calculate the **formal charge** of each atom in the structure. These formal charges won't give the actual charges on the atoms; they'll simply tell us if the atoms are sharing their valence electrons in the "best" way possible, which will happen when the formal charges are all zero (or at least as small as possible). The formula for calculating the formal charge of an atom in a covalent compound is:

$$\text{Formal charge (FC)} = V - \frac{1}{2}B - L$$

where V is the number of valence electrons, B is the number of bonding electrons, and L is the number of lone-paired (non-bonding) electrons. We'll show the calculations of the formal charges for each atom in both Lewis structures:

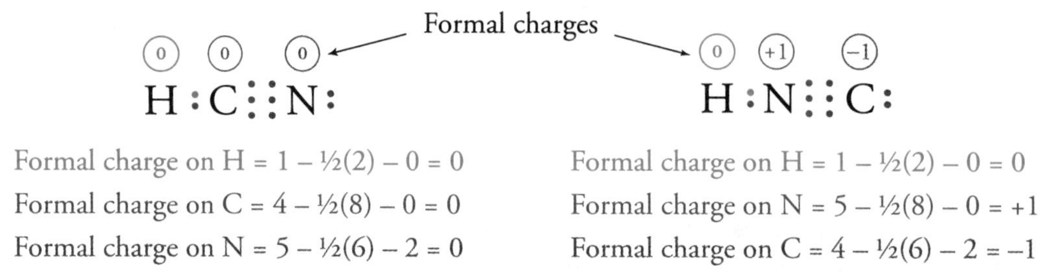

The best Lewis structures have an octet of electrons and a formal charge of zero on all the atoms. (Sometimes, this simply isn't possible, and then the best structure is the one that *minimizes* the magnitudes of the formal charges.) The fact that the HCN structure has formal charges of zero for all the atoms, but the HNC structure does not, tells us right away that the HCN structure is the better one. For dot structures that must contain formal charges on one or more atoms, the best structures have negative formal charges on the more electronegative element.

Example 5-2: What's the formal charge on each atom in phosgene, $COCl_2$?

Solution:

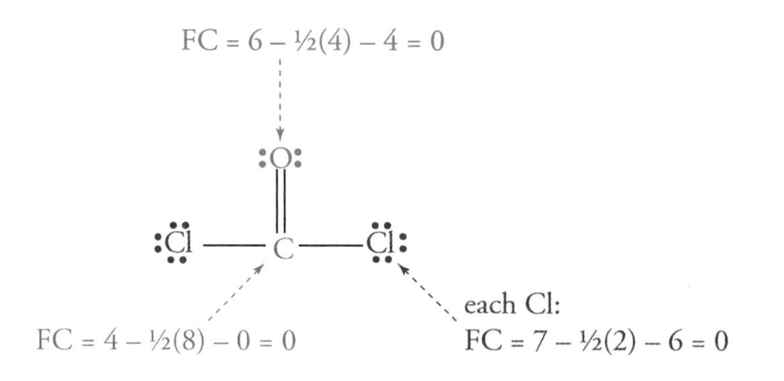

Example 5-3: Which of the following is the best Lewis structure for CH_2O?

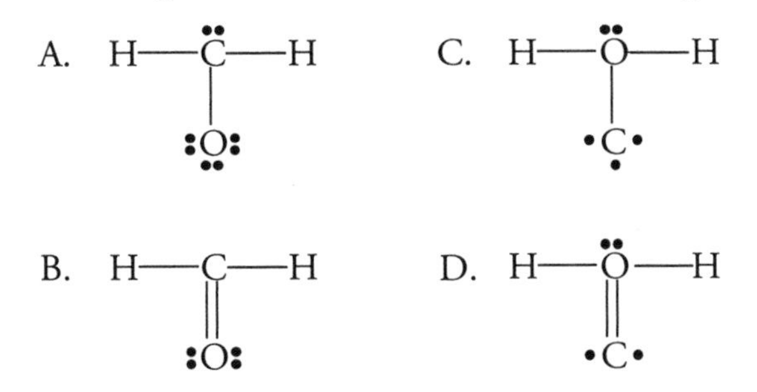

Solution: When faced with a question like this on the MCAT (and they're rather common), the first thing you should do is simply count the electrons. The correct structure for the molecule CH_2O must account for $4 + 2(1) + 6 = 12$ valence electrons. The structure in choice A has 14 and the structure in choice C has 11. Answer choices B and D both have 12 valence electrons. However, in choice D, oxygen is surrounded by 10 total electrons. This is not possible because oxygen, like all elements in the second row of the periodic table, cannot violate the octet rule and exceed 8 valence electrons. Choice B, then, with 12 valence electrons and the least electronegative atom as the central atom, is the best choice.

Resonance

Recall that Lewis dot structures are a model that we use to help us understand where the valence electrons are in a molecule. All models, being simplifications of reality, have limitations, and Lewis dot structures are no exception. Sometimes it is impossible for one structure to accurately represent the reality of a molecule's electron distribution. To account for this complexity, we need two or more structures, called **resonance structures**, to accurately depict the bonding in a molecule. These structures are often needed when there are double or triple bonds in molecules along with one or more lone pairs of electrons.

Let's draw the Lewis structure for sulfur dioxide.

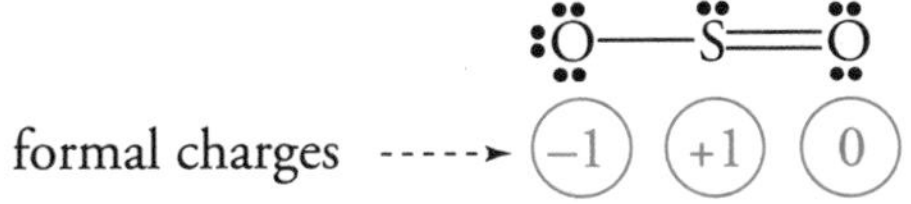

We could also draw the structure like this:

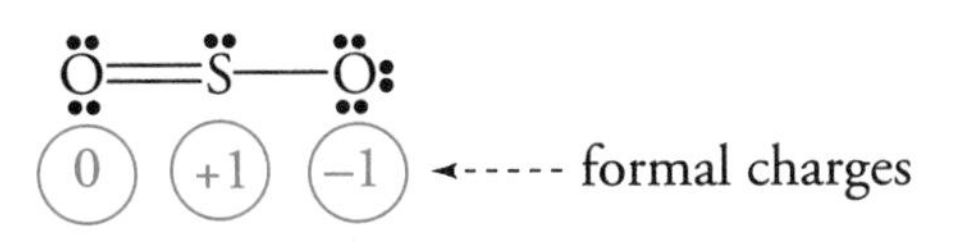

In either case, there's one S—O single bond and one S=O double bond. This would imply that the double-bonded O would be closer to the S atom than the single-bonded O (see Section 5.2, Bond Length and Bond Dissociation Energy). Experiment, however, reveals that the bond lengths are the same. Therefore, to describe this molecule, we say that it's an "average" (or, technically, a **resonance hybrid**) of the equivalent Lewis structures shown:

We can also symbolize the resonance hybrid with a single picture, like this:

The dotted lines in the structure above indicate some double bond character for both S—O bonds, more of a "bond and a half." A molecule may be a resonance hybrid of more than two equivalent Lewis structures; for example, consider the carbonate ion, CO_3^{2-}:

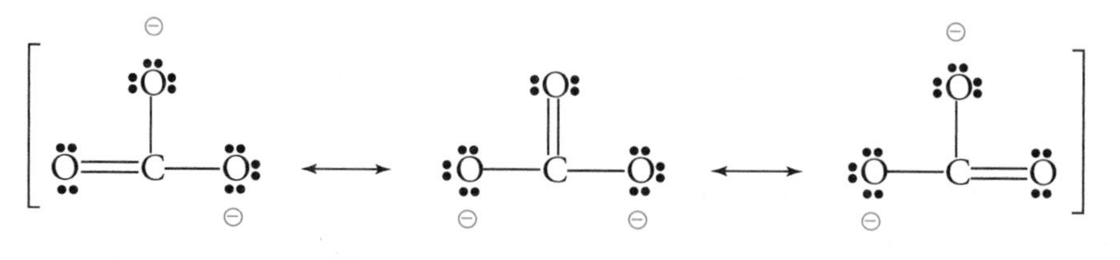

or, more simply,

In addition, a molecule may have two or more non-equivalent resonance structures, and the resonance hybrid is then a weighted average of them, as shown with formaldehyde below:

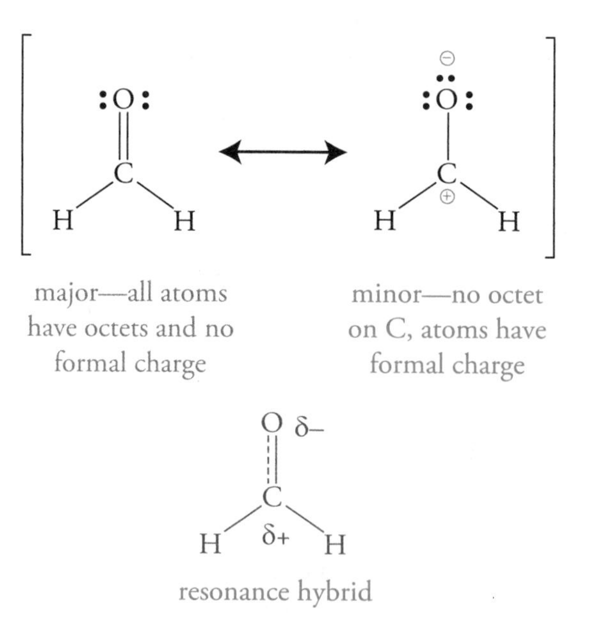

Example 5-4: Resonance structures are two or more structures where:

A) only atoms may move around.
B) only bonding electrons may move around.
C) only nonbonding electrons may move around.
D) only nonbonding electrons, and double and triple bonds may move around.

Solution: Choice D is the correct answer. (This definition is particularly important in organic chemistry.)

5.2 BOND LENGTH AND BOND DISSOCIATION ENERGY

While the term *bond length* makes good intuitive sense (the distance between two nuclei that are bonded to one another), **bond dissociation energy (BDE)** is not quite as intuitive. Bond dissociation energy is the energy required to break a bond *homolytically*. In **homolytic bond cleavage**, one electron of the bond being broken goes to each fragment of the molecule. In this process two radicals form. This is *not* the same thing as **heterolytic bond cleavage** (also known as *dissociation*). In heterolytic bond cleavage, both electrons of the electron pair that make up the bond end up on the same atom; this forms both a cation and an anion.

$$\text{H—F} \xrightarrow[\text{bond cleavage}]{\text{homolytic}} \text{H}\cdot + \cdot\text{F}$$

$$\text{H—F} \xrightarrow[\text{bond cleavage}]{\text{heterolytic}} \text{H}^{\oplus} + \text{F}^{\ominus}$$

These two processes are very different and hence have very different energies associated with them. Here, we will only consider homolytic bond dissociation energies.

When one examines the relationship between bond length and bond dissociation energy for a series of similar bonds, an important trend emerges: For similar bonds, *the higher the bond order, the shorter and stronger the bond.* Bond order is defined as the number of bonds between adjacent atoms, so a single bond has a bond order of 1 while a triple bond has a bond order of 3. The following table, which lists the bond dissociation energies (BDE, in kcal/mol) and the bond lengths (*r*, in angstroms, where 1 Å = 10^{-10} m) for carbon-carbon and carbon-oxygen bonds, illustrates this trend:

	C—C	C=C	C≡C	C—O	C=O	C≡O
BDE (in kcal/mol)	83	144	200	86	191	256
r (in Å)	1.54	1.34	1.20	1.43	1.20	1.13

An important caveat arises because of the varying atomic radii: *bond length/BDE comparisons should only be made for similar bonds.* Thus, carbon-carbon bonds should be compared only to other carbon-carbon bonds; carbon-oxygen bonds should be compared only to other carbon-oxygen bonds, and so on.

Recall the shapes of atomic orbitals: *s* orbitals are spherical about the atomic nucleus, while *p* orbitals are elongated "dumbbell"-shaped about the atomic nucleus.

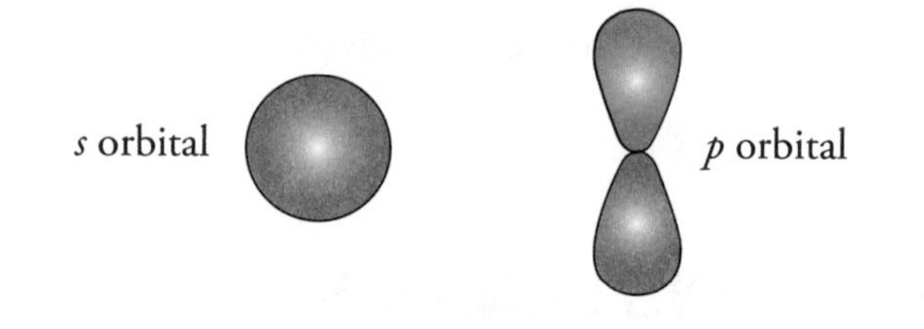

When comparing the same type of bonds, the greater the *s* character in the hybrid orbitals, the shorter the bond (because *s*-orbitals are closer to the nucleus than *p*-orbitals). A greater percentage of *p* character in the hybrid orbital also leads to a more directional hybrid orbital that is farther from the nucleus and thus a longer bond (see section 5.5 for all the details on hybridization). In addition, when comparing the same types of bonds, *the longer the bond, the weaker it is; the shorter the bond, the stronger it is.* In the following diagram, compare all the C—C bonds and all the C—H bonds:

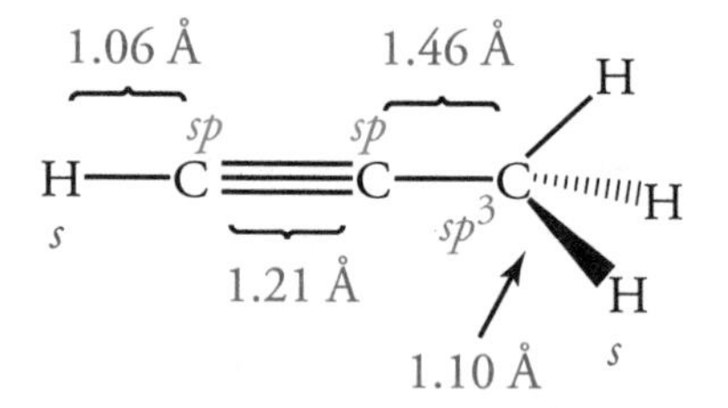

Bond	Bond length	Bond	Bond length
C—C (*sp*–*sp*)	1.21 Å	C–H (*sp*–*s*)	1.06 Å
C—C (*sp*–sp^3)	1.46 Å	C–H (sp^3–*s*)	1.10 Å

5.3 TYPES OF BONDS

Covalent Bonds

A **covalent bond** is formed between atoms when each contributes one or more of its unpaired valence electrons. The electrons are *shared* by both atoms to help complete both octets. There are minor variations in how the electrons are shared, however, so there are several classes of covalent bonds.

Polarity of Covalent Bonds

Recall that electronegativity refers to an atom's ability to attract another atom's valence electrons when it forms a bond. Electronegativity, in other words, is a measure of how much an atom will "hog" the electrons that it's sharing with another atom.

Consider the Lewis dot structures of hydrogen fluoride and fluorine:

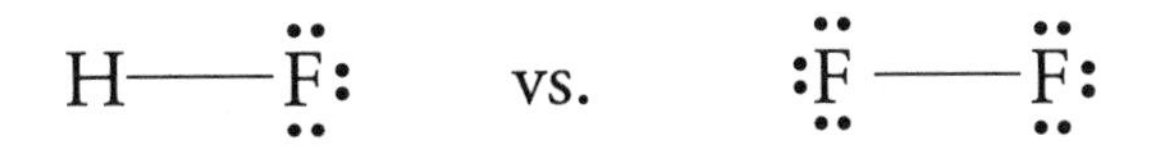

Fluorine is more electronegative than hydrogen (remember the order of electronegativity?), so the electron density will be greater near the fluorine than near the hydrogen in HF. That means that the H—F molecule is partially negative (denoted by δ^-) on the fluorine side and partially positive (denoted by δ^+) on the hydrogen side. We refer to this as **polarity** and say that the molecule has a **dipole moment**. A bond is **polar** if the electron density between the two nuclei is uneven. This occurs if there is a difference in electronegativity of the bonding atoms, and the greater the difference, the more uneven the electron density and the greater the dipole moment.

A bond is **nonpolar** if the electron density between the two nuclei is even. This occurs when there is little to no difference in electronegativity between the bonded atoms, generally when two atoms of the same element are bonded to each other, as we see in F_2.

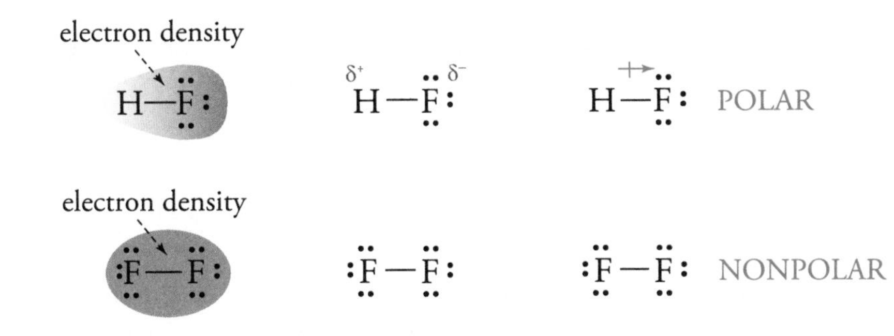

Coordinate Covalent Bonds

Sometimes, one atom will donate *both* of the shared electrons in a bond. That is called a **coordinate covalent bond**. For example, the nitrogen atom in NH_3 donates both electrons in its lone pair to form a bond to the boron atom in the molecule BF_3 to give the coordinate covalent compound F_3BNH_3:

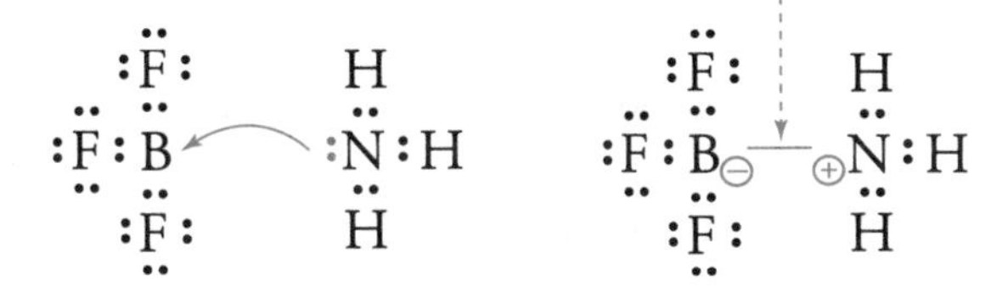

Since the NH_3 molecule donates a pair of electrons, it is known as a **Lewis base.** A Lewis Base can act as a ligand, or a nucleophile (nucleus-loving), and so all three terms are synonymous. Since the BF_3 molecule accepts a pair of electrons, it's known as a **Lewis acid** or **electrophile** (electron loving). When a coordinate covalent bond breaks, the electrons that come from the ligand will leave *with* that ligand.

Example 5-5: Identify the Lewis acid and the Lewis base in the following reaction, which forms a coordination complex:

$$4\ NH_3 + Zn^{2+} \rightarrow Zn(NH_3)_4^{2+}$$

Solution: Each of the NH_3 molecules donates its lone pair to the zinc atom, thus forming four coordinate covalent bonds. Since the zinc ion accepts these electron pairs, it's the Lewis acid; since each ammonia molecule donates an electron pair, they are Lewis bases (or ligands):

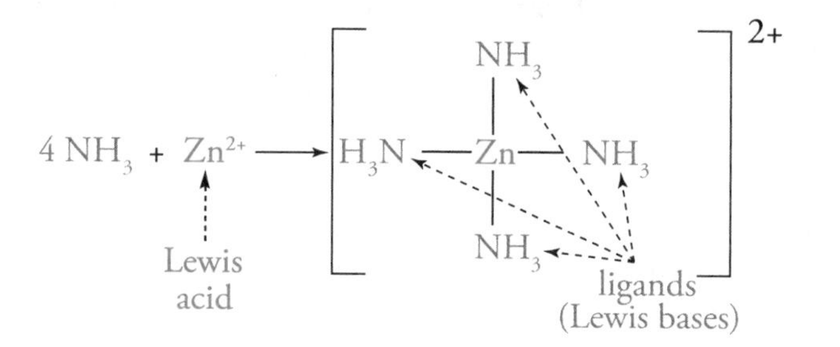

Example 5-6: Which one of the following anions *cannot* behave as a Lewis base/ligand?

A) F^-
B) OH^-
C) NO_3^-
D) BH_4^-

Solution: A Lewis base/ligand is a molecule or ion that donates a pair of nonbonding electrons. So, in order to even be a candidate Lewis base/ligand, a molecule must have a pair of nonbonding electrons in the first place. The ion in choice D does not have any nonbonding electrons.

Example 5-7: Carbon atoms with nonbonding electrons are excellent Lewis bases/ligands. Therefore, which of the following molecules is *not* a potential Lewis base/ligand?

A) CO_2
B) CO
C) CN^-
D) CH_3^-

Solution: The Lewis structures for the given molecules/ions are as follows:

$$O{=}C{=}O \qquad :C{\equiv}O: \qquad :\overset{\ominus}{C}{\equiv}N: \qquad :\overset{\ominus}{C}H_3$$

Therefore, choice A (carbon dioxide) is not a good ligand and is the correct answer here.

Ionic Bonds

While sharing valence electrons is one way atoms can achieve the stable octet configuration, the octet may also be obtained by gaining or losing electrons. For example, a sodium atom will give its valence electron to an atom of chlorine. This results in a sodium cation (Na^+) and a chloride anion (Cl^-), which form sodium chloride. They're held together by the electrostatic attraction between a cation and anion; this is an **ionic bond**.

$$\dot{Na} \; \cdot\ddot{\underset{\cdot\cdot}{Cl}}: \Longrightarrow Na^{\oplus} \; :\ddot{\underset{\cdot\cdot}{Cl}}:^{\ominus}$$

For an ionic bond to form between a metal and a non-metal, there has to be a big difference in electronegativity between the two elements. Generally speaking, the strength of the bond is proportional to the charges on the ions, and it decreases as the ions get farther apart, or as the ionic radii increase. We can use this to estimate the relative strength of ionic systems. For example, consider MgS and NaCl. For MgS, the magnesium ion has a +2 charge and sulfide ion has a –2 charge, while for NaCl, the charges are +1 for sodium and –1 for chloride. Therefore, the MgS "bond" is expected to be about four times stronger than the NaCl "bond," assuming the sizes of the ions are very nearly the same.

Example 5-8: Which of the following is most likely an ionic compound?

A) NO
B) HI
C) ClF
D) KBr

Solution: A diatomic compound is ionic if the electronegativities of the atoms are very different. Of the atoms listed in the choices, those in choice D have the greatest electronegativity difference (K is an alkali metal, and Br is a halogen); K will give up its lone valence electron to Br, forming an ionic bond.

5.4 VSEPR THEORY

The shapes of simple molecules are predicted by **valence shell electron-pair repulsion (VSEPR) theory**. There's one rule: Since electrons repel one another, electron pairs, whether bonding or nonbonding, attempt to move as far apart as possible.

For example, the bonding electrons in beryllium hydride, BeH_2, repel one another and attempt to move as far apart as possible. In this molecule, two pairs of electrons point in opposite directions:

180°

H—Be—H

The angle between the bonds is 180°. A molecule with this shape is said to be linear.

As the BeH_2 example shows, the total number of electron groups on the central atom of a molecule determines its bond angles and *orbital geometry.* Electron groups are defined as any type of bond (single, double, triple) and lone pairs of electrons. Double and triple bonds count only as one electron group, even though they involve two and three pairs of electrons, respectively. To illustrate, the number of electron groups and orbital geometries of the central atom are shown for some example molecules:

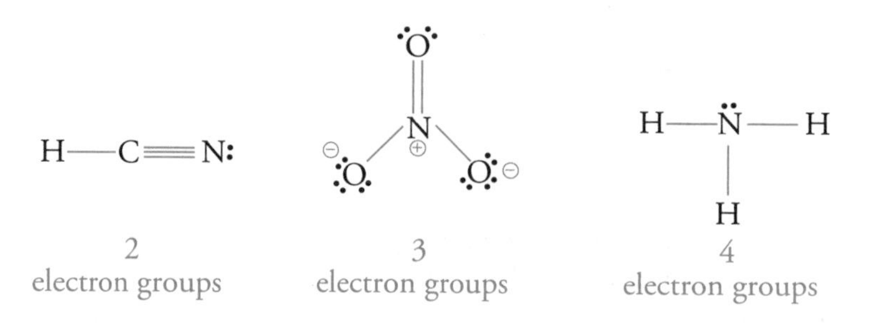

The shape of a molecule (also referred to as the **molecular geometry**) is also a function of the location of the nuclei of its constituent atoms. Therefore, when lone electron pairs are present on the central atom of a molecule, as in NH_3 above, the shape is not the same as the orbital geometry. The table below shows how the presence of lone pairs determines the shape of a molecule:

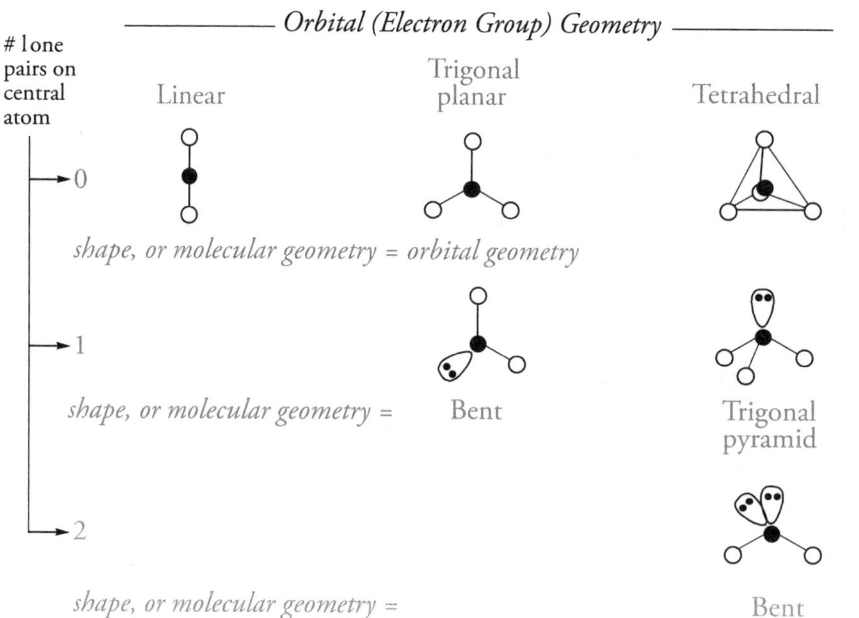

Example 5-9: Determine the orbital geometry and predict the shape of each of the following molecules or ions:

a) H_2O
b) SO_2
c) NH_4^+
d) PCl_3
e) CO_3^{2-}

Solution:

a) H–O–H

orbital geometry: *tetrahedral*
shape: *bent*

b) 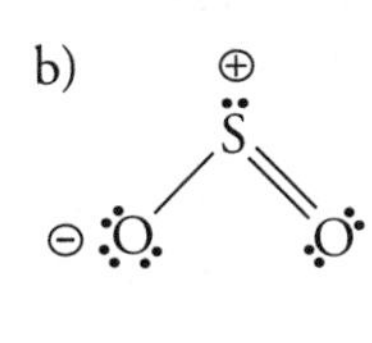

orbital geometry: *trigonal planar*
shape: *bent*

c) 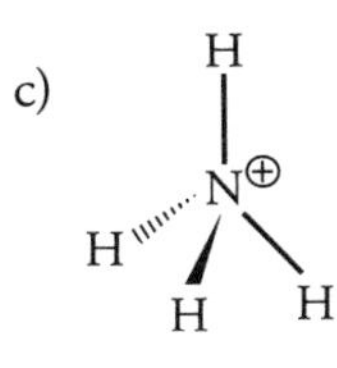

orbital geometry: *tetrahedral*
shape: *tetrahedral*

d) 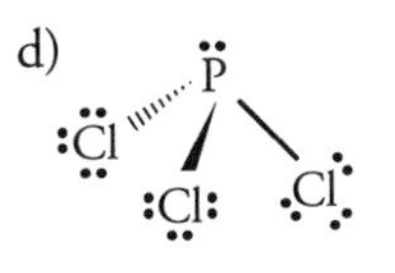

orbital geometry: *tetrahedral*
shape: *trigonal pyramid*

e) 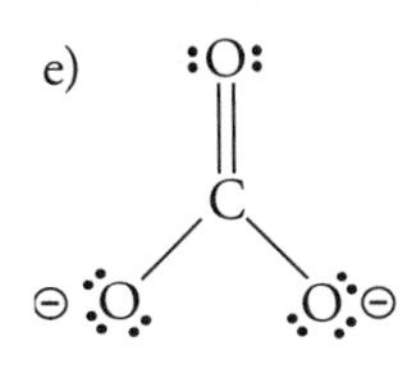

orbital geometry: *trigonal planar*
shape: *trigonal planar*

5.5 HYBRIDIZATION

In order to rationalize observed chemical and structural trends, chemists developed the concept of orbital hybridization. In this model, one imagines a mathematical combination of atomic orbitals centered on the same atom to produce a set of composite, **hybrid** orbitals. For example, consider an *s* and a *p* orbital on an atom.

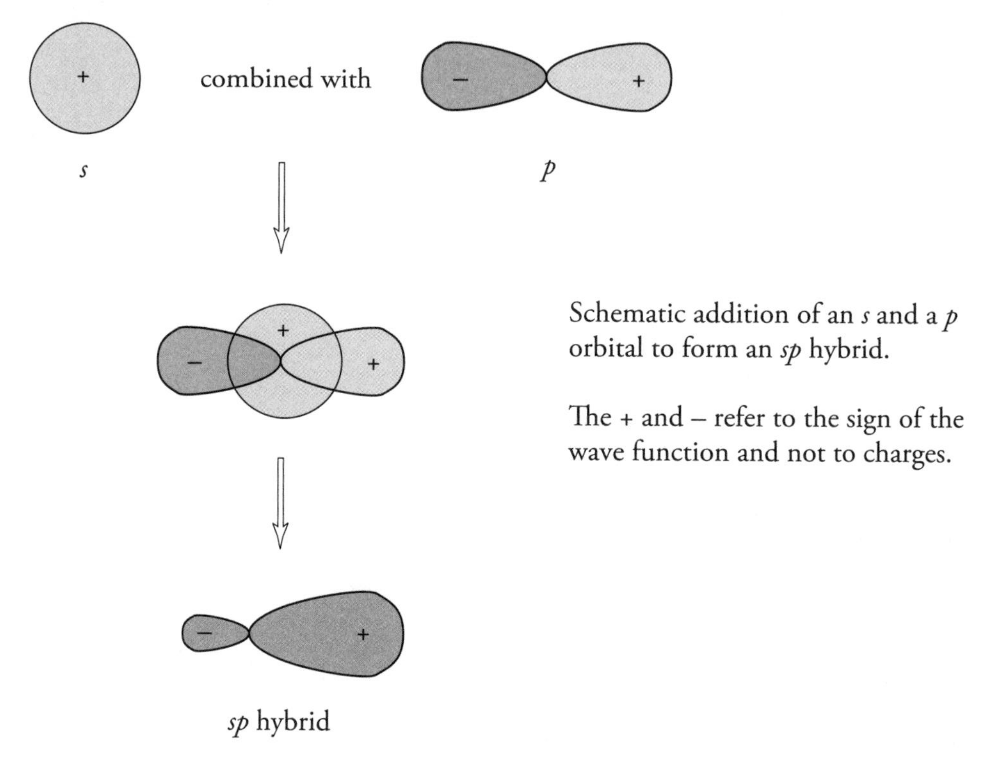

Schematic addition of an *s* and a *p* orbital to form an *sp* hybrid.

The + and – refer to the sign of the wave function and not to charges.

Notice that the new orbital is highly directional; this allows for better overlap when bonding.

There will be two such *sp* hybrid orbitals formed because two orbitals (the *s* and the *p*) were originally combined; that is, the total number of orbitals is conserved in the formation of hybrid orbitals. For this reason, the number of hybrid orbitals on a given atom of hybridization sp^x is $1 + x$ (1 for the *s*, *x* for the *p*'s), where *x* may be either 1, 2, or 3.

The percentages of the *s* character and *p* character in a given sp^x hybrid orbital are listed below:

sp^x hybrid orbital	s character	p character
sp	50%	50%
sp^2	33%	67%
sp^3	25%	75%

To determine the hybridization for most atoms in simple molecules, add the number of attached atoms to the number of non-bonding electron pairs (localized) and use the brief table on the next page (which also gives the ideal bond angles and orbital geometry). The number of attached atoms plus the number of lone pairs is equal to the number of orbitals combined to make the new hybridized orbitals.

Electron Groups (# atoms + # lone pairs)	Hybridization	Bond Angles (ideal)	Orbital Geometry
2	*sp*	180°	linear
3	sp^2	120°	trigonal planar
4	sp^3	109.5°	tetrahedral

5.5

sp hybridization:

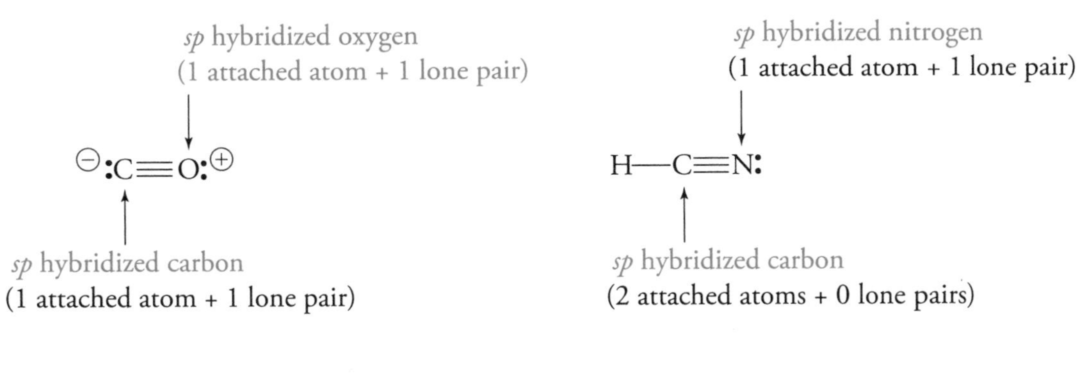

sp^2 hybridization:

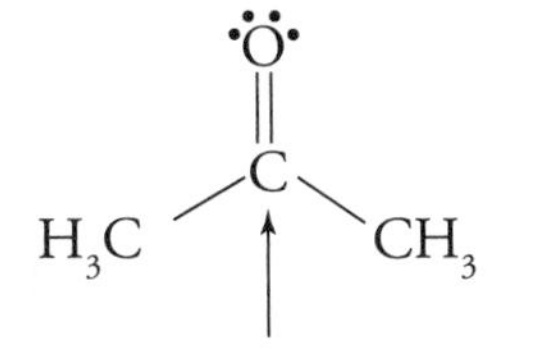

sp^2 hybridized carbon
(3 attached atoms + 0 lone pairs)

H N C H CH_3

sp^2 hybridized nitrogen
(2 attached atoms + 1 lone pair)

sp^3 hybridization:

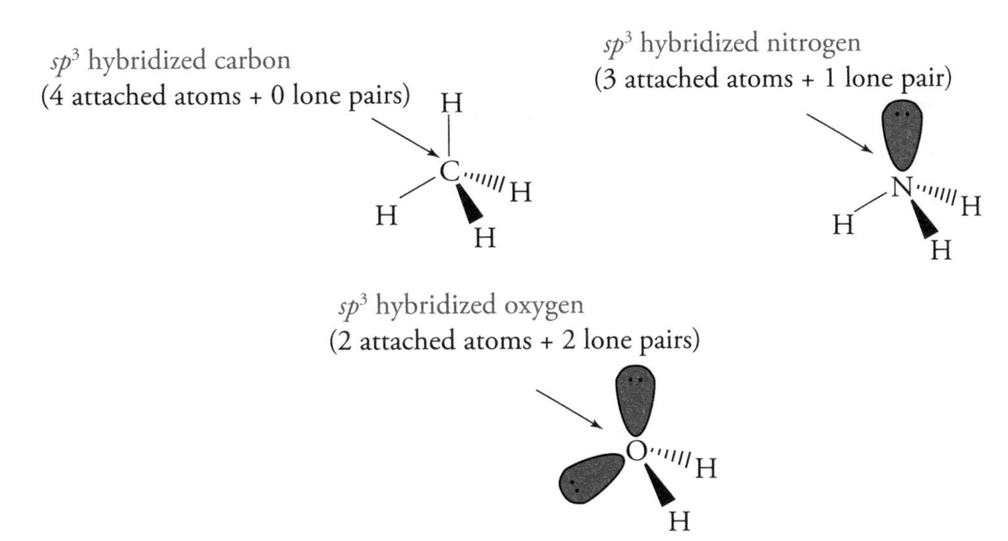

Example 5-10: Determine the hybridization of the central atom in each of the following molecules or ions from the previous example:

a) H_2O
b) SO_2
c) NH_4^+
d) PCl_3
e) CO_3^{2-}

Solution:

a) Hybridization of O is sp^3.
b) Hybridization of S is sp^2.
c) Hybridization of N is sp^3.
d) Hybridization of P is sp^3.
e) Hybridization of C is sp^2.

Sigma (σ) Bonds

A σ **bond** consists of two electrons that are localized between two nuclei. It is formed by the end-to-end overlap of one hybridized orbital (or an *s* orbital in the case of hydrogen) from each of the two atoms participating in the bond. Below, we show the σ bonds in ethane, C_2H_6:

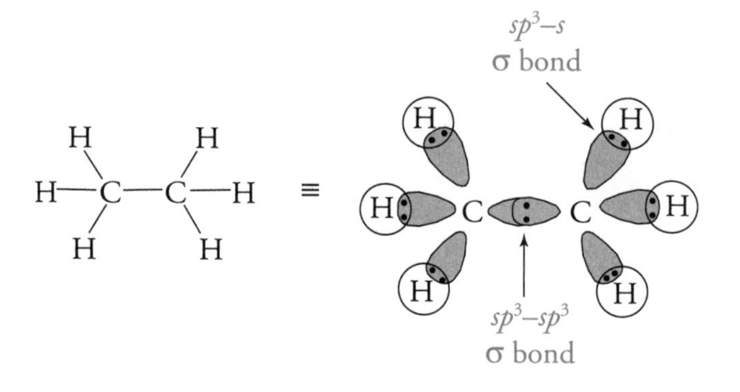

Remember that an sp^3 carbon atom has 4 sp^3 hybrid orbitals, which are derived from one *s* orbital and three *p* orbitals.

Example 5-11: Label the hybridization of the orbitals comprising the σ bonds in the molecules shown below:

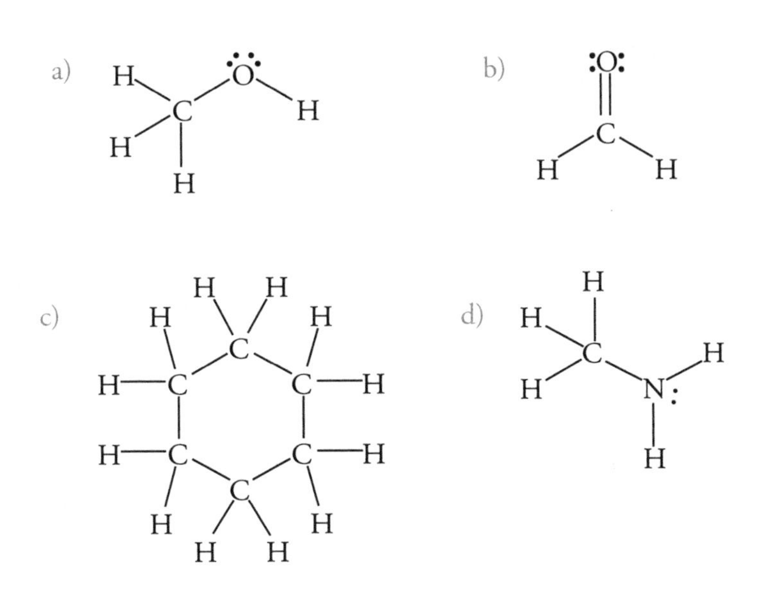

Solution:

a) Bonds to H are sp^3—s σ bonds. The C—O bond is an sp^3—sp^3 σ bond.
b) The bonds to H are sp^2—s σ bonds. The C=O bond contains an sp^2—sp^2 σ bond. (It's also composed of a π bond, which we'll discuss in the next section.)
c) All C—C bonds are sp^3—sp^3 σ bonds, while all C—H bonds are sp^3—s σ bonds.
d) All bonds to H are sp^3—s σ bonds. The C—N bond is an sp^3—sp^3 σ bond.

Pi (π) Bonds

A **π bond** is composed of two electrons that are localized to the region that lies on opposite sides of the plane formed by the two bonded nuclei and immediately adjacent atoms, not directly between the two nuclei as with a σ bond. A π bond is formed by the proper, parallel, side-to-side alignment of two unhybridized *p* orbitals on adjacent atoms. (An sp^2 hybridized atom has three sp^2 orbitals—which come from one *s* and two *p* orbitals—plus one *p* orbital that remains unhybridized.) Below, we show the π bonds in ethene, C_2H_4:

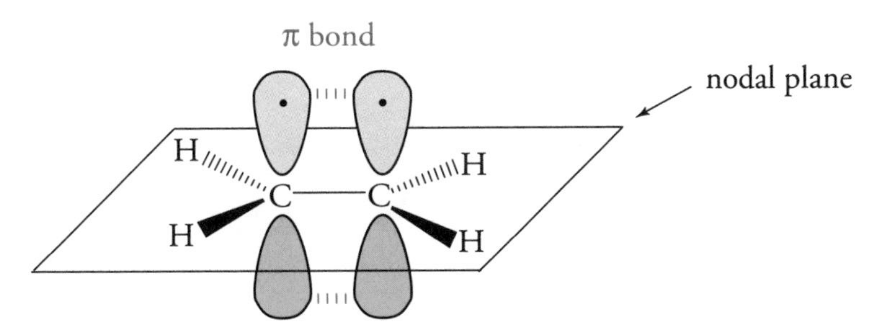

In any multiple bond, *there is only one σ bond; the remainder are π bonds*. Therefore:

a single bond:	composed of 1 σ bond
a double bond:	composed of 1 σ bond and 1 π bond
a triple bond:	composed of 1 σ bond and 2 π bonds

Example 5-12: Count the number of σ bonds and π bonds in each of the following molecules. (Don't forget to count all of the C–H σ bonds!)

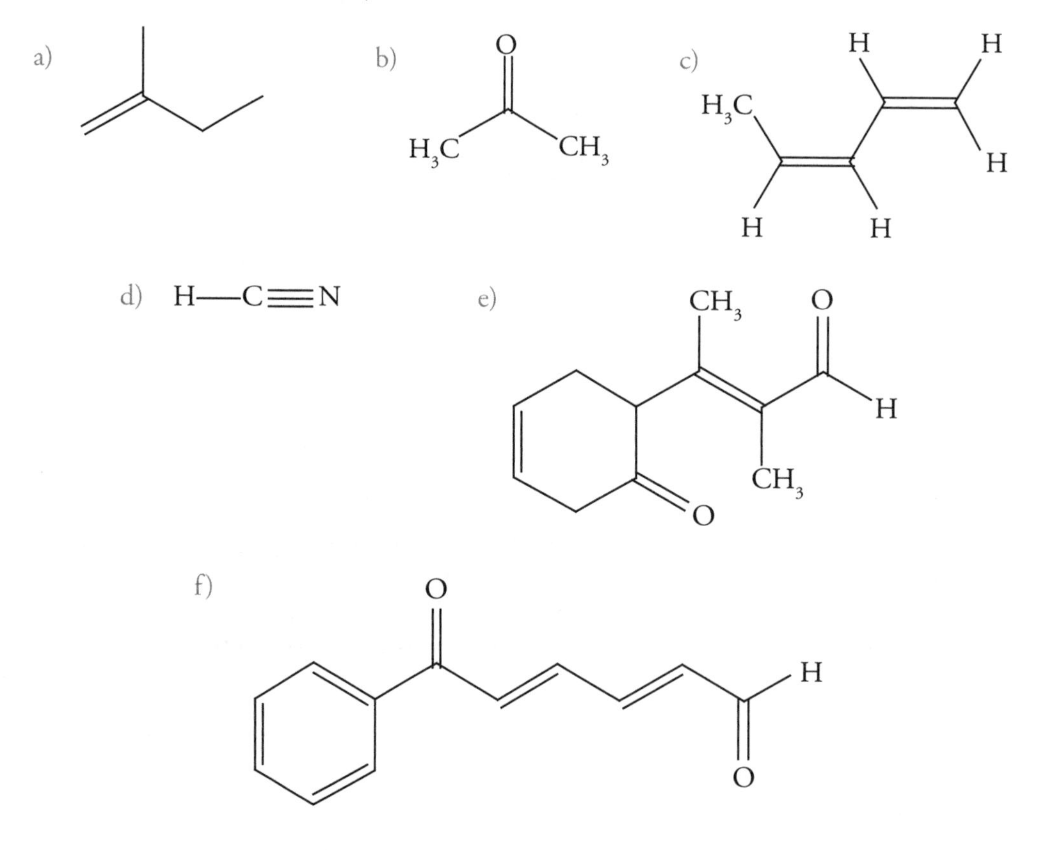

Solution:

a) 14 σ, 1 π
b) 9 σ, 1 π
c) 12 σ, 2 π
d) 2 σ, 2 π
e) 27 σ, 4 π
f) 24 σ, 7 π

5.6 MOLECULAR POLARITY

A molecule as a whole may also be polar or nonpolar. If a molecule contains no polar bonds, it cannot be polar. In addition, if a molecule contains two or more symmetrically oriented polar bonds, the bond dipoles effectively cancel each other out, evenly distributing the electron density over the entire molecule. However, if the polar bonds in a molecule are not symmetrically oriented around the central atom (generally, though not always due to the presence of a lone pair of electrons on the central atom), the individual bond dipoles will not cancel. Therefore, there will be an uneven distribution of electron density over the entire molecule, and this results in a polar molecule.

Example 5-13: For each of the molecules N_2, OCS, and CCl_4, describe the polarity of each bond and of the molecule as a whole.

Solution:

- The N≡N bond is nonpolar (since it's a bond between two identical atoms), and since this *is* the molecule, it's nonpolar, too; no dipole moment.
- For the molecule O=C=S, each bond is polar, since it connects two different atoms of unequal electronegativities. Furthermore, the O=C bond is more polar that then C=S bond, because the difference between the electronegativities of O and C is greater than the difference between the electronegativities of C and S. Therefore, the molecule as a whole is polar (that is, it has a dipole moment):

O=C=S ⟹ O=C=S

polar bonds   polar molecule

- For the molecule CCl_4, each bond is polar, since it connects two different atoms of unequal electronegativities. However, the bonds are symmetrically arranged around the central C atom, leaving the molecule as a whole nonpolar, with no dipole moment:

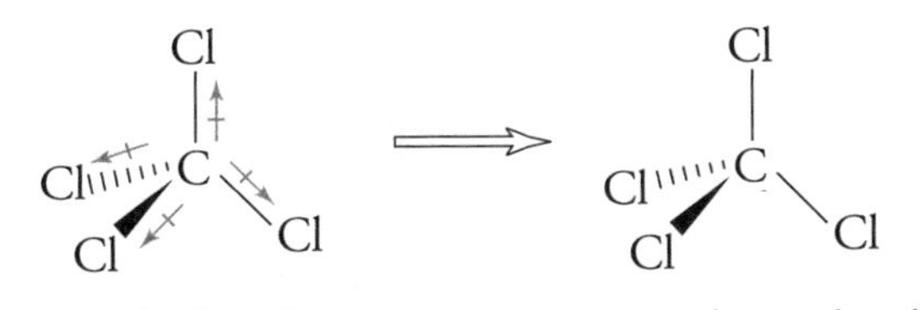

polar bonds   non-polar molecule

5.7 INTERMOLECULAR FORCES

Liquids and solids are held together by intermolecular forces, such as dipole-dipole forces and London dispersion forces. **Intermolecular forces** are the relatively weak interactions that take place between neutral molecules.

Polar molecules are attracted to ions, producing **ion-dipole** forces. **Dipole-dipole forces** are the attractions between the positive end of one polar molecule and the negative end of another polar molecule. (Hydrogen bonding [which we will look at more closely below] is the strongest dipole-dipole force.) A permanent dipole in one molecule may induce a dipole in a neighboring nonpolar molecule, producing a momentary **dipole-induced dipole force.**

Finally, an instantaneous dipole in a nonpolar molecule may induce a dipole in a neighboring nonpolar molecule. The resulting attractions are known as **London dispersion forces**, which are very weak and transient interactions between the instantaneous dipoles in nonpolar molecules. They are the weakest of all intermolecular interactions, and they're the "default" force; all an atom or molecule needs to experience them is electrons. In addition, as the size (molecular weight) of the molecule increases, so does its number of electrons, which increases its polarizability. As a result, the partial charges of the induced dipoles get larger, so the strength of the dispersion forces increases.

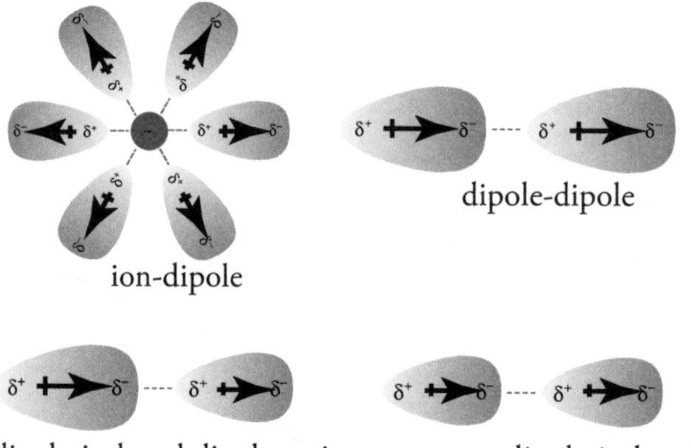

Despite being weak, all intermolecular forces, including London dispersion forces, can have a profound impact on the physical properties of a particular molecule. Specifically, substances with stronger intermolecular forces will exhibit greater melting points, greater boiling points, greater viscosities, and lower vapor pressures (more on this below) than similar compounds with weaker intermolecular forces. For example, many substances that experience only dispersion forces, like fluorine (F_2) and chlorine (Cl_2), exist as gases under standard conditions (1 atm and 25°C). However, bromine (Br_2) is a liquid and iodine (I_2) is a solid because the strength of the dispersion forces increase as atomic size increases.

A final note: Dipole forces, hydrogen bonding, and London forces are *all* collectively known as **van der Waals forces.** However, you may sometimes see the term "van der Waals forces" used to mean only London dispersion forces.

Hydrogen Bonding

Hydrogen bonding is the strongest type of intermolecular force between neutral molecules. In order for a hydrogen bond to form, two very specific criteria must be fulfilled: 1) a molecule must have a covalent bond between H and either N, O, or F, and 2) another molecule must have a lone pair of electrons on an N, O, or F atom. A very common example of a substance that experiences hydrogen bonding is water:

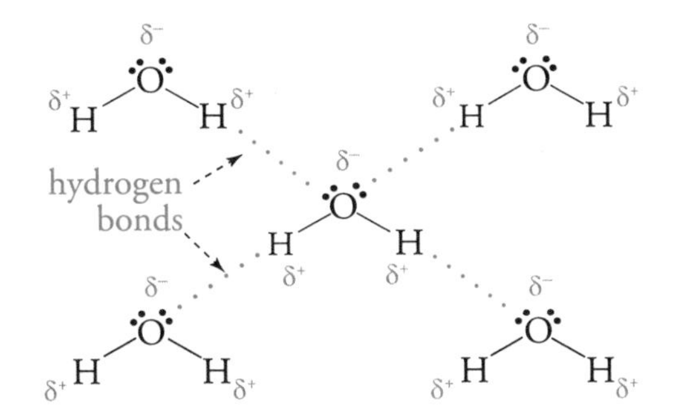

One of the consequences of hydrogen bonding is the high boiling points of compounds such as NH_3, H_2O, and HF. The boiling points of these hydrogen-containing compounds are higher than those of the hydrogen-containing compounds of other elements from Groups V, VI, and VII (the groups where N, O, and F reside). For example, the boiling point of H_2S is approximately –50°C, while that of H_2O is (of course) 100°C.

Example 5-14: Identify the mixture of compounds that *cannot* experience hydrogen bonding with each other:

A) NH_3/H_2O
B) H_2O/HF
C) HF/CO_2
D) H_2S/HCl

Solution: Hydrogen bonding occurs when an H covalently bonded to an F, O, or N electrostatically interacts with another F, O, or N (which doesn't need to have an H). Therefore, choices A, B, and C can all experience hydrogen bonding. Choice D, however, cannot, and this is the answer.

Vapor Pressure

One of the physical properties determined by the strength of the intermolecular forces of a substance is its vapor pressure. **Vapor pressure** is the pressure exerted by the gaseous phase of a liquid that evaporated from the exposed surface of the liquid. The weaker a substance's intermolecular forces, the higher its vapor pressure and the more easily it evaporates. For example, if we compare diethyl ether ($H_5C_2OC_2H_5$) and water, we notice that while water undergoes hydrogen bonding, diethyl ether does not, so despite its greater molecular mass, diethyl ether will vaporize more easily and have a higher vapor pressure than water. Easily vaporized liquids—liquids with *high* vapor pressures—like diethyl ether are said to be **volatile**.

While a substance's vapor pressure is determined in part by its intermolecular forces, vapor pressure is also temperature dependent and increases with the temperature of the substance. Increasing the average kinetic energy of the particles (which is proportional to temperature), allows them to overcome the intermolecular forces holding them together and increases the proportion of particles that can move into the gas phase. As a result, the vapor pressure of a substance is indirectly related to its boiling point, a topic we'll discuss in more detail in Chapter 7.

Example 5-15: An understanding of intermolecular forces is of critical importance because they govern so many physical properties of a substance. The property *least* likely to be influenced by intermolecular force strength is:

A) color.
B) melting point.
C) solubility.
D) vapor pressure.

Solution: Any physical property that involves separating molecules from one another will very much depend upon the strength of intermolecular forces. Molecules are spread out during melting (choice B), dissolving (choice C), and evaporation (choice D). Choice A is therefore the best choice here.

5.8 TYPES OF SOLIDS

Ionic Solids

An **ionic solid** is held together by the electrostatic attraction between cations and anions in a lattice structure. The bonds that hold all the ions together in the crystal lattice are the same as the bonds that hold each pair of ions together. Ionic bonds are strong, and most ionic substances (like NaCl and other salts) are solid at room temperature. As discussed previously, the strength of the bonds is primarily dependent on the magnitudes of the ion charges, and to a lesser extent, the size of the ions. The greater the charge, the stronger the force of attraction between the ions. The smaller the ions, the more they are attracted to each other.

Network Solids

In a **network solid**, atoms are connected in a **lattice** of covalent bonds, meaning that all interactions between atoms are covalent bonds. Like in an ionic solid, in a network solid the *inter*molecular forces are identical to the *intra*molecular forces. You can think of a network solid as one big molecule; in a network solid there are only intramolecular forces. As a result, network solids are very strong, and tend to be very hard solids at room temperature. Diamond (one of the allotropes of carbon) and quartz (a form of silica, SiO_2) are examples of network solids.

Metallic Solids

A sample of metal can be thought of as a covalently bound lattice of nuclei and their inner shell electrons, surrounded by a "sea" or "cloud" of electrons. At least one valence electron per atom is not bound to any one particular atom and is free to move throughout the lattice. These freely roaming valence electrons are called **conduction electrons.** As a result, metals are excellent conductors of electricity and heat, and are malleable and ductile. Metallic bonds vary widely in strength, but almost all metals are solids at room temperature.

Molecular Solids

The particles at the lattice points of a crystal of a molecular solid are molecules. These molecules are held together by one of three types of *inter*molecular interactions—hydrogen bonds, dipole-dipole forces, or London dispersion forces. Since these forces are *significantly* weaker than ionic, network, or metallic bonds, molecular compounds typically have much lower melting and boiling points than the other types of solids above. Molecular solids are often liquids or gases at room temperature, and are more likely to be solids as the strength of their intermolecular forces increase.

Example 5-16: Of the following, which one will have the lowest melting point?

A) MgO
B) CH_4
C) Cr
D) HF

Solution: Almost all ionic compounds are solids at room temperature. Therefore, choice A is eliminated. Similarly, all metals except for mercury (Hg) are solids at room temperature, so eliminate choice C. Both answers B and D will be molecular solids. Hydrogen fluoride is able to hydrogen bond and will therefore have stronger intermolecular interactions than the nonpolar methane. Since choice B has the weakest intermolecular forces (London dispersion), it will be easiest to melt.

Chapter 5 Summary

- The best Lewis dot or resonance structures have 1) octets around all atoms, 2) minimized formal charge, and 3) negative charges on more electronegative elements.
- Covalent bonds form between elements with similar electronegativities (two nonmetals).
- Nonpolar bonding means equal electron sharing; polar bonding means unequal electron sharing, and electron density is higher around the more electronegative element.
- Coordinate covalent bonds form between a Lewis base (e^- pair donor) and a Lewis acid (e^- pair acceptor); electrons are shared.
- Ionic bonds form between elements with large differences in electronegativity (metals + nonmetals), and the strength of that bond depends on the charge and the size of the ions. Larger charges and smaller ions make the strongest ionic bonds.
- VSEPR theory predicts the shape of molecules; angles between electron groups around the central atom are maximized for greatest stability.
- The hybridization of an atom is dependent on the number of electron groups on the atom (two e^- groups = sp, three e^- groups = sp^2, four e^- groups = sp^3).
- Sigma (σ) bonds generally form through the end-on-end overlap of hybrid orbitals; pi (π) bonds form through the side-to-side overlap of unhybridized *p* orbitals.
- If bond dipoles are symmetrically oriented in a molecule, the molecule as a whole is nonpolar; if the dipoles are asymmetrical, the molecule will be polar.
- Intermolecular forces are cohesive, and determine the physical properties (melting and boiling points, solubility, vapor pressure, etc.) of a compound based on relative strengths.
- While all molecules have London dispersion forces, they are the predominant intermolecular force that holds nonpolar molecules together. Dipole-dipole forces are the predominant intermolecular force that holds polar molecules together.
- Molecules with an H—F, H—O, or H—N bond and an N, O, or F with a lone electron pair can hydrogen bond.

CHAPTER 5 FREESTANDING PRACTICE QUESTIONS

1. Which of these molecules has the strongest dipole moment?

A) PBr_3O
B) PF_5
C) CCl_4
D) SF_6

2. A pure sample of which of the following ions/molecules will participate in intermolecular hydrogen bonding?

I. CH_3CO_2H
II. CO_2
III. H_2S

A) I only
B) III only
C) I and II
D) I and III

3. Which of the following best describes the intramolecular bonding present within a cyanide ion (CN^-)?

A) Ionic bonding
B) Covalent bonding
C) Van der Waals forces
D) Induced dipole

4. All of the following would be categorized as having tetrahedral orbital geometry EXCEPT:

A) NH_3
B) NH_4^+
C) CO_2
D) CH_4

5. Rank the following from highest to lowest boiling point:

I. H_2SO_4
II. NH_3
III. CO_2
IV. H_2O

A) I > IV > II > III
B) II > I > IV > III
C) I > III > IV > II
D) IV > III > I > II

6. Which of the following most specifically accounts for neon's ability to form a solid at 1 atm and 25 K?

A) Gravitational forces
B) Electrostatic forces
C) London dispersion forces
D) Strong nuclear forces

7. In the following reaction, which of the following most accurately describes the type of bond formed?

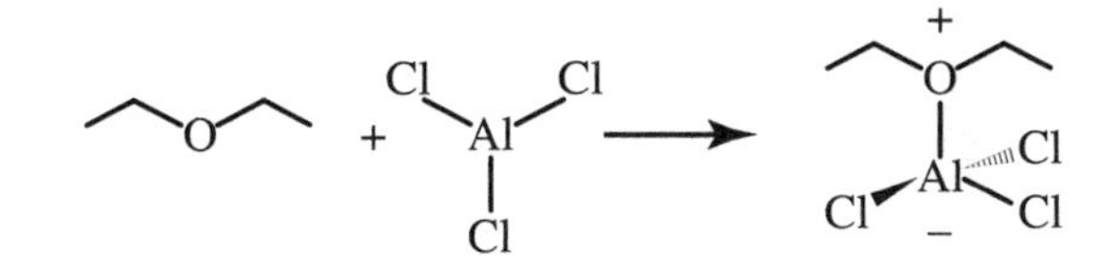

A) Covalent
B) Electrostatic
C) Metallic
D) Coordinate covalent

CHAPTER 5 PRACTICE PASSAGE

Metallic mercury, mercury salts, and organometallic mercury compounds are now recognized as critical toxins, but have historically been introduced into the environment through a number of industrial processes. The noted neurotoxicity of the element stems in part from its inhibition of cellular mechanisms that control oxidative damage. The brain is particularly sensitive to these effects, as the amount of oxygen consumed in the organ is large and thus the potential for oxidative damage is high.

Many standard elemental testing procedures for mercury, such as flame atomic absorption spectroscopy, are unable to differentiate between the three aforementioned types of mercury (metallic, ionic, organometallic). Since biological effects of each form are different, especially in acute dosages, a process has been developed for the separation of the three varieties of mercury (Figure 1), and is used primarily for detection of mercury in soil samples.

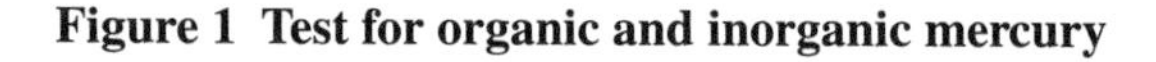

Figure 1 Test for organic and inorganic mercury

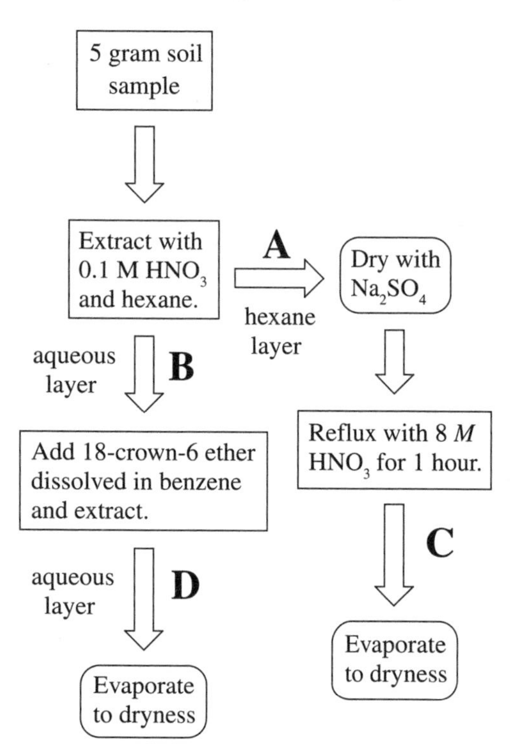

The first step is to extract a 5-gram soil sample with 50 mL of hexane and 50 mL of dilute nitric acid. The organic layer is removed, dried, and then refluxed with a 1:1 mixture of *conc.* HNO_3 and water. The water layer is removed, evaporated to dryness, and then quantitatively analyzed using AA (Atomic Absorption Spectroscopy).

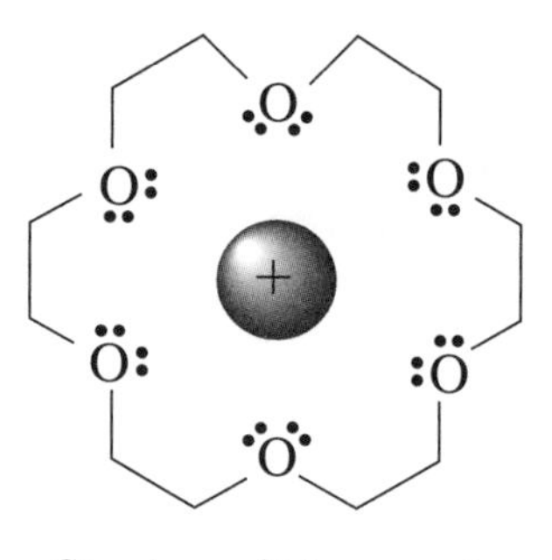

Structure of 18-crown-6 ether with chelated cation

The aqueous layer in the first extract is treated with 0.5 gram of a crown ether dissolved in benzene. The purpose of the crown ether is to chelate large radius cations present in solution (such as sodium, potassium, calcium, and barium) and carry them into the organic layer. The crown ether 18-crown-6, so named as it consists of an 18-membered ring with 6 oxygen atoms, was found to be ideal for the chelation of the large mercury cation. This bilayer solution is shaken and then separated. The aqueous layer is evaporated to dryness, and then analyzed via AA.

1. Assume that the cation in the crown ether is a potassium ion. What is the charge of the crown ether–K^+ complex?

A) –1
B) 0
C) +1
D) Greater than zero but less than one

2. In which solution(s) would you find $(CH_3)_2Hg$?

A) Solution A only
B) Solutions A and C
C) Solution B only
D) Solutions B and D

3. Based upon information presented in the passage, which of the following statements is NOT true?

A) The ionic radius of mercury is not equal to the radius of K^+.
B) Insoluble mercury salts have a greater solubility in solutions of nitric acid.
C) Crown ethers increase the organic solubility of cations by encapsulating the ion with a relatively nonpolar shell.
D) Mercury salts are highly volatile.

4. Which of the following methods might be used to separate ionic Zn^{2+} contamination from the Hg-containing material in the aqueous layer after extraction step B?

A) Add 15-crown-5 ether and extract with an organic phase.
B) Fractionally distill Zn from the solution.
C) Add a strong alkylating agent, such as $LiCH_3$ and extract with an organic phase.
D) Add 21-crown-7 ether and extract with an organic phase.

5. What is the purpose of refluxing the hexane solution with 8 *M* nitric acid for one hour?

A) To reduce all organometallic compounds to methane and metal.
B) To oxidize all organometallic compounds to CO_2, water, and metal ions.
C) To nitrate (i.e., create R–NO_2 groups in) the organometallic compounds.
D) To increase the hydrophobic nature of organometallic compounds.

SOLUTIONS TO CHAPTER 5 FREESTANDING PRACTICE QUESTIONS

1. **A** A bond has a dipole moment when the two atoms involved in the bond differ in electronegativity. However, an entire molecule can only have a dipole if it contains bond dipoles and is asymmetrical. Choice A is tetrahedral and not all four substituents are the same. Therefore, it is asymmetrical and has a small negative dipole in the direction of the most electronegative substituent, oxygen. The remaining choices are trigonal bipyramidal, tetrahedral, and octahedral respectively. All have identical substituents, are symmetrical, and have no net dipole moment.

2. **A** In order to participate in intermolecular hydrogen bonding, a molecule must be able to act as both a hydrogen bond donor and acceptor. In order to act as a hydrogen bond donor, a molecule must possess a hydrogen (H) atom covalently bound to a nitrogen (N), oxygen (O), or fluorine (F) atom. In order to act as a hydrogen bond acceptor, a molecule must have an oxygen, nitrogen, or fluorine atom with an unshared pair of electrons. CH_3CO_2H meets both of these requirements, and is therefore a valid choice. CO_2 does not possess any hydrogen atoms and is therefore an invalid option. While H_2S may seem like an enticing choice, sulfur is not sufficiently electronegative to produce hydrogen bonding when covalently bound to hydrogen atoms.

3. **B** Van der Waals forces and induced dipoles are both examples of intermolecular forces, not intramolecular bonding, therefore choices C and D can be eliminated. The disparity in electronegativities between the carbon (C) and nitrogen (N) atoms in cyanide is not sufficient enough to produce ionic bonding, therefore choice B, covalent bonding, is the best answer.

$$:N\equiv C:^{\ominus}$$

4. **C** The central atom, N, possesses three bonding electron groups and one lone pair of electrons. NH_3 therefore has tetrahedral orbital geometry.

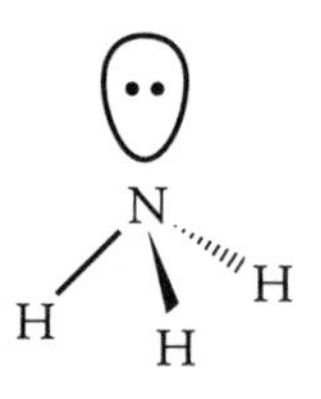

The central atom, N, possesses four bonding electron groups and zero lone pairs. NH_4^+ therefore has tetrahedral geometry.

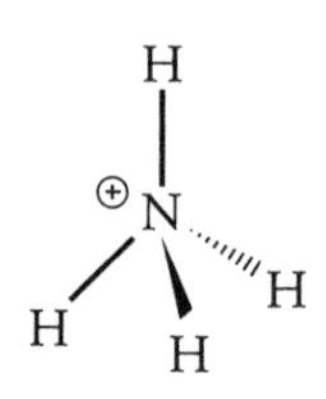

The central atom, C, possesses two bonding electron groups and zero lone pairs. Recall that double bonds count as a single electron group. CO_2 therefore has linear geometry.

O=C=O

The central atom, C, possesses four bonding electron groups and zero lone pairs. CH_4 therefore has tetrahedral geometry.

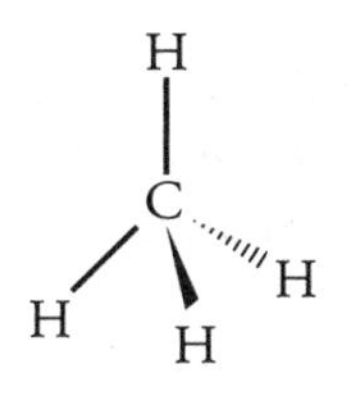

5. **A** When answering ranking questions, it is best to determine the extremes and eliminate answer choices. Of the four molecules, only H_2O and H_2SO_4 are liquids at room temperature, and therefore would have higher boiling points than the two gases. Both experience strong hydrogen bonding, but the H_2SO_4 molecule is substantially larger, and, aside from this, has more sites to accept H-bonds from surrounding molecules. Therefore, H_2SO_4 should have the highest boiling point, eliminating answer choices B and D. Both NH_3 and CO_2 are gases at room temperature. However, NH_3 experiences hydrogen bonding, and therefore its boiling point would be higher than CO_2, eliminating choice C and making choice A the correct answer.

6. **C** For neon to form a solid, there must be intermolecular forces holding the atoms or molecules in relatively fixed positions. Gravitational force is given by $F = G\frac{m_1 m_2}{r^2}$. With the constant G on the order of 10^{-11} and the mass of neon on the order of 10^{-26}, this force is negligible and choice A is eliminated. Electrostatic force is given by $F = k\frac{q_1 q_2}{r^2}$. Choice B is incorrect because neon is a neutral atom without any charge, so there are no significant electrostatic forces at play. Choice D is incorrect because strong nuclear forces act over a very small distance essentially limited to the size of the nucleus. Choice C is correct. Neon is a neutral molecule and has induced dipole-dipole interactions, also known as London dispersion forces. Because this is the weakest of the van der Waals forces, neon must be cooled down close to absolute zero before forming a solid.

7. **D** This is an example of a Lewis acid-base reaction. In this type of reaction, one species accepts an electron pair from another species and a coordinate covalent bond is formed. One member of the bond donates *both* electrons in the bond. Whereas a coordinate covalent bond is a type of covalent interaction, the questions asks for the best answer, and coordinate covalent is more specific (eliminate choice A). Therefore, choice D is correct. An electrostatic bond is an ionic bond (eliminate choice B), and a metallic bond involves long-range delocalization of valence electrons, which is not the case in the product molecule (eliminate choice C).

SOLUTIONS TO CHAPTER 5 PRACTICE PASSAGE

1. **C** By giving the structure, the passage indicates that the crown ether molecule is neutral. Since the charge of the potassium ion is +1, than the total charge of the complex is 0 + (+1) = +1.

2. **A** Dimethyl mercury is a nonpolar molecule. So in the very first extraction, it will preferentially dissolve in the hexane solution (solution A). However, later, this solution is refluxed with nitric acid, a powerful oxidizing agent, which oxidizes dimethyl mercury into CO_2, H_2O, and Hg^{2+} (as the nitrate). Like other metal nitrates, mercuric nitrate is water soluble and is then found in the aqueous portion of the solution (solution C). (This is why you keep the aqueous layer for the analysis!) So dimethyl mercury will only be found in solution A.

3. **D** Choices A, B, and C are all correct statements.

   A: The radius of Hg^{2+} is much smaller than that of K^+ because of ion contraction—2+ ions contract more than 1+ ions do. However, you should have been able to reason that the sizes of the potassium and mercury ions had to be different because 18-crown-6 ether, a polydentate ligand, will chelate any metal ion which snugly fits within the ring. 18-crown-6 ether chelated potassium ions, but evidently left the mercuric ions in the aqueous phase.

   B: The soil sample was extracted with 0.1 *M* HNO_3 for this reason. Since most soils are frequently washed through rainfall, almost all soluble salts are leached out of the soil. Hence, any mercury salts which remain in the soil must be of the insoluble type. So through the addition of HNO_3, these salts are solubilized.

   C: This is how and why crown ethers act to carry highly hydrophilic cations into hydrophobic solvents. Thus, crown ethers can be extremely toxic because of their ability to deposit toxic, heavy metal ions in bad places (just as outlined in the explanation of question 2 above).

   D: This is not true. Almost all ionic compound are solids at room temperature, and have extremely low volatilities.

4. **A** The meaning behind the naming scheme for crown ethers is given in the passage. 18-Crown-6 ether is an 18-membered ring with 6 oxygen atoms, and is stated as being the ideal fit for the very large mercury ion. 15-Crown-5 ether, a 15 membered ring with 5 oxygens, is smaller, and as it is less ideal for mercury it might be safely assumed it is better for smaller cations, such as Zn^{2+}. Extraction with this smaller ether should preferentially complex zinc, leaving the mercury behind in the aqueous phase. Choice D suggests using a larger ether to remove a smaller cation, which does not make sense (eliminate choice D). Fractional distillation of Zn salts from an aqueous solution is not viable, as salts have an insignificant vapor pressure at reasonably achievable temperatures (eliminate choice B). A strong alkylating agent would be expected to make both organozinc and organomercury compounds, which would both favor an organic phase (eliminate choice C).

5. **B** Choice A is not true; nitric acid, one of the grand masters of oxidizing agents, will never reduce anything! Choice C is not so bad since HNO_3 is actually used to nitrate alcohols and electrophilic functional groups such as aromatic rings and alkenes. Unfortunately for this choice, there are none of these functionalities in dimethyl mercury. Choice D is wrong and is contrary to the fact that the mercury is found in the aqueous solution after this process. Any highly reduced molecule, such as organometallic compounds, are readily oxidized by hot nitric acid.

Chapter 6
Thermodynamics

6.1 SYSTEM AND SURROUNDINGS

Why does anything happen? Why does a creek flow downhill, a puddle of water evaporate after it rains, a chemical reaction proceed? It's all **thermodynamics:** the transformation of energy from one form to another. The laws of thermodynamics underlie any event in which energy is transformed.

The Zeroth Law of Thermodynamics

The Zeroth Law is often conceptually described as follows: If two systems are both in thermal equilibrium with a third system, then the two initial systems are in thermal equilibrium with one another.

Thus, the Zeroth Law establishes a definition of thermal equilibrium. When systems are in thermal equilibrium with one another, their temperatures must be the same. When bodies of different temperatures are brought into contact with one another, heat will flow from the body with the higher temperature into the body with lower temperature in order to achieve equilibrium at the same temperature value. This means that devices (thermometers) may be designed to achieve thermal equilibrium with their surroundings, and give a quantified, relative value of the temperature at this equilibrium.

In this way, the Zeroth Law defines what we call temperature, and is the logical basis for the subsequent thermodynamic laws that rely on it. It also establishes the link between heat and temperature. An important practical application of the Zeroth Law is calorimetry, which will be discussed in more detail in Chapter 7.

The First Law of Thermodynamics

The First Law states that *the total energy of the universe is constant.* Energy may be transformed from one form to another, but it cannot be created or destroyed.

An important result of the First Law is that an isolated system has a constant energy—no transformation of the energy is possible. When systems are in contact, however, energy is allowed to flow, and thermal equilibrium can be attained. In addition, the First Law also establishes that work can be put into a system to increase its overall energy. This may or may not occur with a corresponding change in temperature. The concept of work and its effects on physical thermodynamics can be examined more closely in the *MCAT Physics and Math Review.*

Conventions Used in Thermodynamics

In thermodynamics we have to designate a "starting line" and a "finish line" to be able to describe how energy flows in chemical reactions and physical changes. To do this we use three distinct designations to describe energy flow: the system, the surroundings, and the thermodynamic universe (or just universe).

The system is the thing we're looking at: a melting ice cube, a solid dissolving into water, a beating heart, anything we want to study. Everything else: the table the ice cube sits on and the surrounding air, the beaker that holds the solid and the water, the chest cavity holding the heart, is known collectively as the surroundings. The system and the surroundings taken together form the thermodynamic universe.

We need to define these terms so that we can assign a direction—and therefore a sign, either (+) or (–)—to energy flow. For chemistry (and for physics), we define everything in terms of what's happening to the *system*.

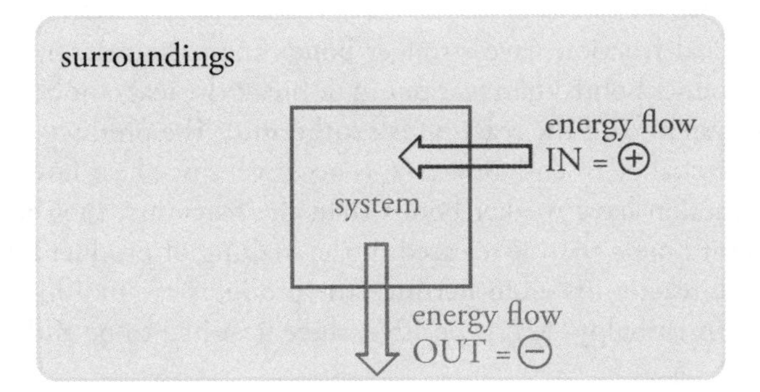

Consider energy flowing from the surroundings into the system, like the heat flowing from the table to the ice cube that's sitting on it. What is happening in the system? As energy flows in (here it's heat), the molecules in the system absorb it and start to jiggle faster. Eventually enough energy is absorbed to cause the ice to melt. Overall, the energy of the system *increased*, and we therefore give it a (+) sign. What about water when it freezes? Here energy (once again, heat) leaves the water (our system), and the jiggling of the water molecules slows down. The energy of the system has *decreased*, and we therefore assign a (–) sign to energy flow. Finally, energy that flows into the system flows out of the surroundings, and energy that flows out of the system flows into the surroundings. Therefore, we can make these statements:

1) When energy flows into a system from the surroundings, the energy of the system increases and the energy of the surroundings decreases.
2) When energy flows out of a system into the surroundings, the energy of the system decreases and the energy of the surroundings increases.

Keep this duality in mind when dealing with energy.

6.2 ENTHALPY

Enthalpy is a measure of the heat energy that is released or absorbed when bonds are broken and formed during a reaction that's run at constant pressure. The symbol for enthalpy is ***H***. Some general principles about enthalpy prevail over all reactions:

- When a bond is formed, energy is released. $\Delta H < 0$.
- Energy must be put into a bond in order to break it. $\Delta H > 0$.

In a chemical reaction, energy must be put into the reactants to break their bonds. Once the reactant bonds are broken, the atoms rearrange to form products. As the product bonds form, energy is released. The enthalpy of a reaction is given by the difference between the enthalpy of the products and the enthalpy of the reactants.

$$\Delta H = H_{\text{products}} - H_{\text{reactants}}$$

The enthalpy change, ΔH, is also known as the **heat of reaction.**

If the products of a chemical reaction have stronger bonds than the reactants, then more energy is released in the making of product bonds than was put in to break the reactant bonds. In this case, energy is released overall from the system, and the reaction is **exothermic**. The products are in a lower energy state than the reactants, and the change in enthalpy, ΔH, is negative, since heat flows out of the system. If the products of a chemical reaction have weaker bonds than the reactants, then more energy is put in during the breaking of reactant bonds than is released in the making of product bonds. In this case, energy is absorbed overall and the reaction is **endothermic**. The products are in a higher energy state than the reactants, and the change in enthalpy, ΔH, is positive, since heat had to be added to the system from the surroundings.

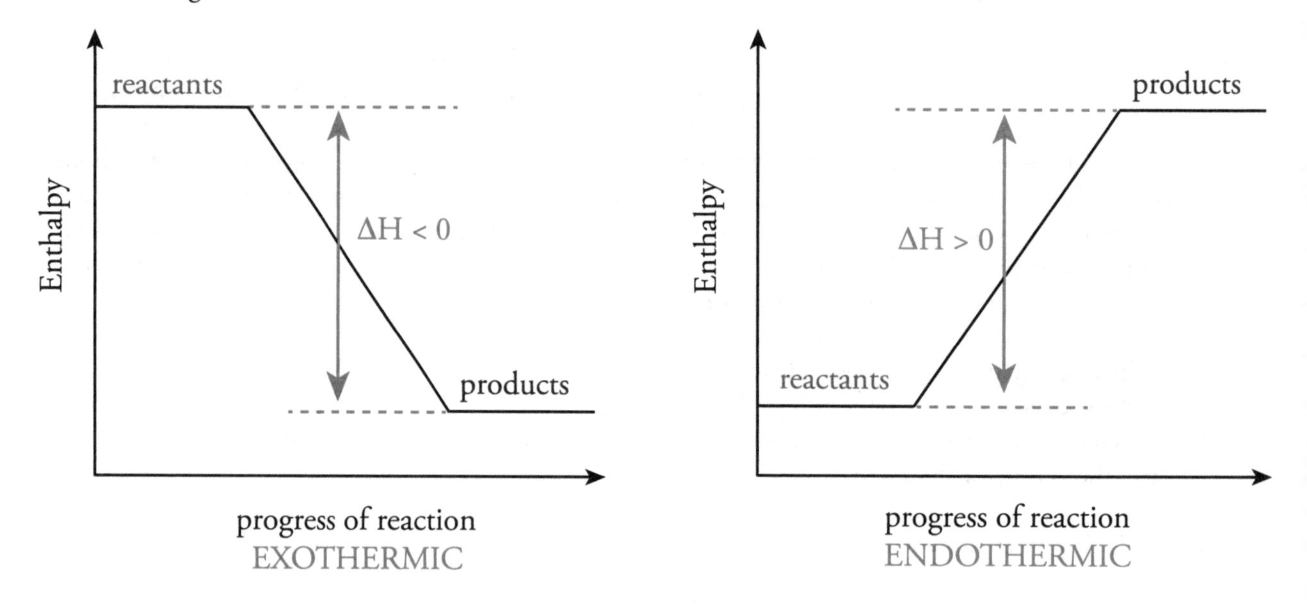

Example 6-1: The combustion of methanol is given by this reaction:

$$2\ CH_3OH(g) + 3\ O_2(g) \rightarrow 2\ CO_2(g) + 4\ H_2O(g), \qquad \Delta H = -1352\text{ kJ}$$

a) How much heat is produced when 16 g of oxygen gas reacts with excess methanol?
b) Is the reaction exothermic or endothermic?
c) How many moles of carbon dioxide are produced when 676 kJ of heat is produced?

Solution:

a) The molecular weight of O_2 is 2(16) = 32 g/mol, so 16 g represents one-half mole. If 1352 kJ of heat is released when 3 moles of O_2 react, then just (1/6)(1352 kJ) = 225 kJ of heat will be released when one-half mole of O_2 reacts.
b) Because ΔH is negative, the reaction is exothermic. And since 6 moles of gaseous products are being formed from just 5 moles of gaseous reactants, the disorder (entropy) has increased.
c) The stoichiometry of the given balanced reaction tells us that 2 moles of CO_2 are produced when 1352 kJ of heat is produced. So, half as much CO_2 (that is, 1 mole) is produced when half as much heat, 676 kJ, is produced.

Example 6-2: Which one of the following processes does NOT contribute to the change in enthalpy, ΔH_{rxn}, of a chemical reaction?

A) Phase change
B) Formation of stronger intermolecular forces
C) Breaking covalent bonds
D) The presence of a heterogeneous catalyst

Solution: A catalyst lowers the activation energy, but does not affect an equilibrium constant, enthalpy, entropy, or free energy in any way. Choice D is the answer. The other choices do fall under the umbrella of enthalpy.

6.3 CALCULATION OF ΔH_{rxn}

The heat of reaction (ΔH_{rxn}) can be calculated in a number of ways. Each of these will lead to the same answer given accurate starting values. The three most important methods to be familiar with are the use of standard heats of formation ($\Delta H°_f$), Hess's law of heat summation, and the summation of average bond enthalpies.

Standard Conditions

Essentially every process is affected by temperature and pressure, so scientists have a convention called **standard conditions** for which most constants, heats of formation, enthalpies, and so on are determined. Under standard conditions, the temperature is 298 K (25°C) and the pressure is 1 atm. All solids and liquids are assumed to be pure, and solutions are considered to be at a concentration of 1 *M*. Values that have been determined under standard conditions are designated by a ° superscript: $\Delta H°$, for example. Be careful not to confuse *standard conditions* with *standard temperature and pressure* (STP). STP is 0°C, while standard conditions means 25°C.

Heat of Formation

The **standard heat of formation,** ΔH°_f, is the amount of energy required to make one mole of a compound *from its constituent elements in their natural or standard state,* which is the way the element exists under standard conditions. The convention is to assign elements in their standard state forms a ΔH°_f of zero. For example, the ΔH°_f of C(*s*) (as graphite) is zero. Diatomic elements, such as O_2, H_2, Cl_2 and so on are also defined as zero, rather than their atomic forms (such as O, Cl, etc.), because the diatomic state is the *natural* state for these elements at standard conditions. For example, $\Delta H^\circ_f = 0$ for O_2, but for O, $\Delta H^\circ_f = 249$ kJ/mol at standard conditions, because it takes energy to break the O=O double bond.

When the ΔH°_f of a compound is positive, then an input of heat is required to make that compound from its constituent elements. When ΔH°_f is negative, making the compound from its elements gives off energy.

You can calculate the ΔH° of a reaction if you know the heats of formation of the reactants and products:

$$\Delta H^\circ_{rxn} = (\Sigma n \times \Delta H^\circ_{f,\ products}) - (\Sigma n \times \Delta H^\circ_{f,\ reactants})$$

In the above equation "*n*" denotes the stoichiometric coefficient applied to each species in a chemical reaction as written. ΔH°_f of a given compound is the heat needed to form one mole, and as such if two moles of a molecule are needed to balance a reaction one must double the corresponding ΔH°_f in the enthalpy equation. If only half a mole is required one must divide the ΔH°_f by 2.

Example 6-3: Which of the following substances does NOT have a heat of formation equal to zero at standard conditions?

A) $F_2(g)$
B) $Cl_2(g)$
C) $Br_2(g)$
D) $I_2(s)$

Solution: Heat of formation, ΔH°_f, is zero for a pure element in its natural phase at standard conditions. All of the choices are in their standard state, except for bromine, which is a liquid, not a gas, at standard conditions. The correct answer is C.

Example 6-4: What is ΔH° for the following reaction under standard conditions if the ΔH°_f of $CH_4(g) = -75$ kJ/mol, ΔH°_f of $CO_2(g) = -393$ kJ/mol, and ΔH°_f of $H_2O(l) = -286$ kJ/mol?

$$CH_4(g) + 2\ O_2(g) \rightarrow CO_2(g) + 2\ H_2O(l)$$

Solution: Using the equation for ΔH°_{rxn}, we find that

$$\Delta H^\circ_{rxn} = (\Delta H^\circ_f CO_2 + 2\ \Delta H^\circ_f H_2O) - (\Delta H^\circ_f CH_4 + 2\ \Delta H^\circ_f O_2)$$

$$= (-393\ \text{kJ/mol} + 2(-286)\ \text{kJ/mol}) - (-75\ \text{kJ/mol} + 0\ \text{kJ/mol})$$

$$= -890\ \text{kJ/mol}$$

Hess's Law of Heat Summation

Hess's law states that if a reaction occurs in several steps, then the sum of the energies absorbed or given off in all the steps will be the same as that for the overall reaction. This is due to the fact that enthalpy is a state function, which means that changes are independent of the pathway of the reaction. Therefore, ΔH is independent of the pathway of the reaction.

For example, we can consider the combustion of carbon to form carbon monoxide to proceed by a two-step process:

1) $C(s) + O_2(g) \rightarrow CO_2(g)$ $\quad \Delta H_1 = -394$ kJ
2) $CO_2(g) \rightarrow CO(g) + 1/2\ O_2(g)$ $\quad \Delta H_2 = +283$ kJ

To get the overall reaction, we add the two steps:

$$C(s) + 1/2\ O_2(g) \rightarrow CO(g)$$

So, to find ΔH for the overall reaction, we just add the enthalpies of each of the steps:

$$\Delta H_{rxn} = \Delta H_1 + \Delta H_2 = -394 \text{ kJ} + 283 \text{ kJ} = -111 \text{ kJ}$$

It's important to remember the following two rules when using Hess's law:

1) *If a reaction is reversed, the sign of ΔH is reversed too.*
   For example, for the reaction $CO_2(g) \rightarrow C(s) + O_2(g)$, we'd have $\Delta H = +394$ kJ.

2) *If an equation is multiplied by a coefficient, then ΔH must be multiplied by that same value.*
   For example, for $1/2\ C(s) + 1/2\ O_2(g) \rightarrow 1/2\ CO_2(g)$, we'd have $\Delta H = -197$ kJ.

Summation of Average Bond Enthalpies

Enthalpy itself can be viewed as the energy stored in the chemical bonds of a compound. Bonds have characteristic enthalpies that denote how much energy is required to break them homolytically (often called the bond dissociation energy, or BDE; see Section 5.2).

As indicated at the start of this section, an important distinction should be made here in the difference in sign of ΔH for making a bond versus breaking a bond. One must, necessarily, infuse energy into a system to break a chemical bond. As such the ΔH for this process is positive, making it endothermic. On the other hand, creating a bond between two atoms must have a negative value of ΔH. It therefore gives off heat and is exothermic. If this weren't the case it would indicate that the bonded atoms were higher in energy than they were when unbound; such a bond would be unstable and immediately dissociate.

Therefore we have a very important relation that can help you on the MCAT:

> Energy is needed to break a bond.
>
> Energy is released in making a bond.

From this we come to the third method of determining ΔH_{rxn}. If a question provides a list of bond enthalpies, ΔH_{rxn} can be determined through the following equation:

$$\Delta H_{rxn} = \Sigma \text{ (BDE bonds broken)} - \Sigma \text{ (BDE bonds formed)}$$

One can see that if stronger bonds are being formed than those being broken, then ΔH_{rxn} will be negative. More energy is released than supplied and the reaction is exothermic. If the opposite is true and breaking strong bonds takes more energy than is regained through the making of weaker product bonds, then the reaction is endothermic.

Example 6-5: Given the table of average bond dissociation energies below, calculate ΔH_{rxn} for the combustion of methane given in Example 6-4.

Bond	Average Bond Dissociation Energy (kJ/mol)
C—H	413
O—H	467
C=O	799
C=N	615
H—Cl	427
O=O	495

A) 824 kJ/mol
B) 110 kJ/mol
C) –824 kJ/mol
D) –110 kJ/mol

Solution: First determine how many of each type of bond are broken in the reactants and formed in the products based on the stoichiometry of the balanced equation. Then using the bond dissociation energies we can calculate the enthalpy change:

$$\Delta H_{rxn} = \Sigma \text{ (BDE bonds broken)} - \Sigma \text{ (BDE bonds formed)}$$

$$\Delta H_{rxn} = (4(\text{C—H}) + 2(\text{O=O})) - (2(\text{C=O}) + 4(\text{O—H}))$$

$$= (4(413) + 2(495)) - (2(799) + 4(467))$$

$$= -824 \text{ kJ/mol}$$

The correct answer is C. You may notice that the two methods of calculating the reaction enthalpy for the same reaction did not produce exactly the same answer. This is due to the fact that bond energies are reported as the average of many examples of that type of bond, whereas heats of formation are determined for each individual chemical compound. The exact energy of a bond will be dependent not only on the two atoms bonded together but also the chemical environment in which they reside. The average bond energy gives an approximation of the strength of an individual bond, and as such, the summation of bond energies give an approximation of ΔH_{rxn}.

6.4 ENTROPY

The Second Law of Thermodynamics

There are several different ways to state the **second law of thermodynamics**, each appropriate to the particular system under study, but they're all equivalent. One way to state this law is that the disorder of the universe increases in a spontaneous process. For this to make sense, let's examine what we mean by the term *spontaneous*. For example, water will spontaneously splash and flow down a waterfall, but it will not spontaneously collect itself at the bottom and flow up the cliff. A bouncing ball will come to rest, but a ball at rest will not suddenly start bouncing. If the ball is warm enough, it's got the energy to start moving, but heat—the disorganized, random kinetic energy of the constituent atoms—will not spontaneously organize itself and give the ball an overall kinetic energy to start it moving. From another perspective, heat will spontaneously flow from a plate of hot food to its cooler surroundings, but thermal energy in the cool surroundings will not spontaneously concentrate itself and flow into the food. None of these processes would violate the first law, but they do violate the second law.

Nature has a tendency to become increasingly disorganized, and another way to state the second law is that *all processes tend to run in a direction that leads to maximum disorder*. Think about spilling milk from a glass. Does the milk ever collect itself together and refill the glass? No, it spreads out randomly over the table and floor. In fact, it needed the glass in the first place just to have any shape at all. Likewise, think about the helium in a balloon: It expands to fill its container, and if we empty the balloon, the helium diffuses randomly throughout the room. The reverse doesn't happen. Helium atoms don't collect themselves from the atmosphere and move into a closed container. The natural tendency of *all* things is to increase their disorder.

We measure disorder or randomness as **entropy**. The greater the disorder of a system, the greater is its entropy. Entropy is represented by the symbol S, and the change in entropy during a reaction is represented by the symbol ΔS. The change in entropy is determined by the equation

$$\Delta S = S_{\text{products}} - S_{\text{reactants}}$$

If randomness increases—or order decreases—during the reaction, then ΔS is positive for the reaction. If randomness decreases—or order increases—then ΔS is negative. For example, let's look at the decomposition reaction for carbonic acid:

$$H_2CO_3 \rightleftharpoons H_2O + CO_2$$

In this case, one molecule breaks into two molecules, and disorder is increased. That is, the atoms are less organized in the water and carbon dioxide molecules than they are in the carbonic acid molecule. The entropy is increasing for the forward reaction. Let's look at the reverse process: If CO_2 and H_2O come together to form H_2CO_3, we've decreased entropy because the atoms in two molecules have become more organized by forming one molecule.

In general, entropy is predictable in many cases:

- Liquids have more entropy than solids.
- Gases have more entropy than solids or liquids.
- Particles in solution have more entropy than undissolved solids.
- Two moles of a substance have more entropy than one mole.
- The value of ΔS for a reverse reaction has the same magnitude as that of the forward reaction, but with opposite sign: $\Delta S_{\text{reverse}} = -\Delta S_{\text{forward}}$.

While the overall drive of nature is to increase entropy, reactions can occur in which entropy decreases, but we must either put in energy or gain energy from making more stable bonds. (We'll explore this further when we discuss Gibbs free energy.)

Example 6-6: Which of the following processes would have a negative ΔS?

A) The evaporation of a liquid.
B) The freezing of a liquid.
C) The melting of a solid.
D) The sublimation of a solid.

Solution: Only the change described in choice B involves a decrease in randomness—the molecules of a solid are more ordered and organized than those in a liquid. So this process would have a negative change in entropy.

Example 6-7: Of the following reactions, which would have the greatest positive entropy change?

A) $2\ NO(g) + O_2(g) \rightarrow 2\ NO_2(g)$
B) $2\ HCl(aq) + Mg(s) \rightarrow MgCl_2(aq) + H_2(g)$
C) $2\ H_2O\ (g) + Br_2(g) + SO_2(g) \rightarrow 2\ HBr\ (g) + H_2SO_4(aq)$
D) $2\ I^-(aq) + Cl_2(g) \rightarrow I_2(s) + 2\ Cl^-(aq)$

Solution: The reactions in choices A, C, and D all describe processes involving a decrease in randomness, that is, an increase in order. However, the process in choice B has a highly ordered solid on the left, but a highly disordered gas on the right, so we'd expect this reaction to have a positive entropy change.

Example 6-8: For the endothermic reaction

$$2\ CO_2(g) \rightarrow 2\ CO(g) + O_2(g)$$

which of the following is true?

A) ΔH is positive, and ΔS is positive.
B) ΔH is positive, and ΔS is negative.
C) ΔH is negative, and ΔS is positive.
D) ΔH is negative, and ΔS is negative.

Solution: Since we're told that the reaction is endothermic, we know that ΔH is positive. This eliminates choices C and D. Now, what about ΔS? Has the disorder increased or decreased? On the reactant side, we have one type of gas molecule, while on the right we have two. The reaction increases the numbers of gas molecules, so this describes an increase in disorder. ΔS is positive, and the answer is A.

Example 6-9: A gas is observed to undergo condensation. Which of the following is true about the process?

A) ΔH is positive, and ΔS is positive.
B) ΔH is positive, and ΔS is negative.
C) ΔH is negative, and ΔS is positive.
D) ΔH is negative, and ΔS is negative.

Solution: Condensation is the phase change from gas to liquid, which *releases* heat (since the reverse process, vaporization, requires an input of heat). Therefore, ΔH is negative, and choices A and B are eliminated. Now, because the change from gas to liquid represents an increase in order—since gases are so highly disordered—this process will have a negative change in entropy. The answer is therefore D.

The Third Law of Thermodynamics

The Third Law defines absolute zero to be a state of zero-entropy. At absolute zero, thermal energy is absent and only the least energetic thermodynamic state is available to the system in question. If only one state is possible, then there is no randomness to the system and $S = 0$. In this way, the Third Law describes the least thermally energetic state, and therefore the lowest achievable temperature. Kelvin defined the temperature at this state as 0 on his temperature scale.

6.5 GIBBS FREE ENERGY

The magnitude of the change in **Gibbs free energy**, ΔG, is the energy that's available (free) to do useful work from a chemical reaction. The spontaneity of a reaction is determined by changes in enthalpy and in entropy, and G includes both of these quantities. Now we have a way to determine whether a given reaction will be spontaneous. In some cases—namely, when ΔH and ΔS have different signs—it's easy. For example, if ΔH is negative and ΔS is positive, then the reaction will certainly be spontaneous (because the products have less energy and more disorder than the reactants; there are two tendencies for a spontaneous reaction: to decrease enthalpy and/or to increase entropy). If ΔH is positive and ΔS is negative, then the reaction will certainly be nonspontaneous (because the products would have more energy and less disorder than the reactants).

But what happens when ΔH and ΔS have the *same* sign? Which factor—enthalpy or entropy—will dominate and determine the spontaneity of the reaction? The sign of the single quantity ΔG will dictate whether or not a process is spontaneous, and we calculate ΔG from this equation:

Change in Gibbs Free Energy

$$\Delta G = \Delta H - T\Delta S$$

where T is the absolute temperature (in kelvins). And now, we can then say this:

- $\Delta G < 0 \rightarrow$ spontaneous in the forward direction
- $\Delta G = 0 \rightarrow$ reaction is at equilibrium
- $\Delta G > 0 \rightarrow$ nonspontaneous in the forward direction

If ΔG for a reaction is positive, then the value of ΔG for the *reverse* reaction has the same magnitude but is negative. Therefore, the reverse reaction is spontaneous.

ΔG and Temperature

The equation for ΔG shows us that the entropy ($T\Delta S$) term depends directly on temperature. At low temperatures, the entropy doesn't have much influence on the free energy, and ΔH is the dominant factor in determining spontaneity. But as the temperature increases, the entropy term becomes more significant relative to ΔH and can dominate the value for ΔG. In general, the universe tends towards increasing disorder (positive ΔS) and stable bonds (negative ΔH), and a favorable combination of these will make a process spontaneous. The following chart summarizes the combinations of ΔH and ΔS that determine ΔG and spontaneity.

ΔH	ΔS	ΔG	**Reaction is...?**
–	+	–	spontaneous
+	+	– at sufficiently high T + at low T	spontaneous nonspontaneous
–	–	+ at high T – at sufficiently low T	nonspontaneous spontaneous
+	–	+	nonspontaneous

Important note: While values of ΔH are usually reported in terms of kJ, values of ΔS are usually given in terms of J. When using the equation $\Delta G = \Delta H - T\Delta S$, make sure that your ΔH and ΔS are expressed *both* in kJ or *both* in J.

Example 6-10: What must be true about a spontaneous, endothermic reaction?

A) ΔH is negative.
B) ΔG is positive.
C) ΔS is positive.
D) ΔS is negative.

Solution: Since the reaction is spontaneous, we know that ΔG is negative, and since we know the reaction is endothermic, we also know that ΔH is positive. The equation $\Delta G = \Delta H - T\Delta S$ then tells us that ΔS must be positive, choice C.

Example 6-11: If it's discovered that a certain nonspontaneous reaction becomes spontaneous if the temperature is lowered, then which of the following must be true?

A) ΔS is negative and ΔH is positive.
B) ΔS is negative and ΔH is negative.
C) ΔS is positive and ΔH is positive.
D) ΔS is positive and ΔH is negative.

Solution: If the temperature at which the reaction takes place has an impact on the spontaneity of the reaction, that means that the signs of ΔH and ΔS must both be either positive or negative (eliminate choices A and D). Lowering the temperature term makes the $T\Delta S$ term a smaller value in magnitude, and changes the sign of ΔG from positive to negative. That must mean that the ΔH is a negative value, as its impact is now more obvious at the new lower temperature, making choice B the correct answer.

6.6 REACTION ENERGY DIAGRAMS

A chemical reaction can be graphed as it progresses in a reaction energy diagram. True to its name, a reaction energy diagram plots the free energy of the total reactions versus the conversion of reactants to products.

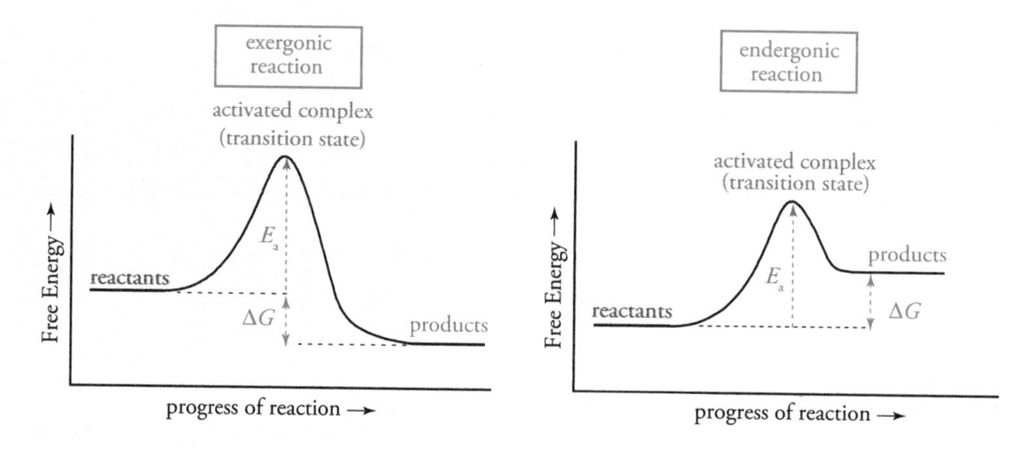

The ΔG of the overall reaction is the difference between the energy of the products and the energy of the reactants: $\Delta G_{rxn} = G_{products} - G_{reactants}$. When the value of $T\Delta S$ is very small, then ΔG can approximate ΔH, with the difference between the energy of products and reactants being very close to the heat of reaction, ΔH.

The activation energy, E_a, is the extra energy the reactants required to overcome the activation barrier, and determines the kinetics of the reaction. The higher the barrier, the slower the reaction proceeds towards equilibrium; the lower the barrier, the faster the reaction proceeds towards equilibrium. However, E_a does *not* determine the equilibrium, and an eternally slow reaction (very big E_a) can have a very favorable (large) K_{eq}. Many more details of both kinetics and equilibrium will be discussed in Chapters 9 and 10, respectively.

Kinetics vs. Thermodynamics

Just because a reaction is thermodynamically favorable (i.e., *spontaneous*), does not automatically mean that it will be taking place rapidly. **Do not confuse kinetics with thermodynamics** (this is something the MCAT will *try* to get you to do many times!). They are separate realms. *Thermodynamics predicts the spontaneity (and the equilibrium) of reactions, not their rates.* If you had a starting line and a finish line, thermodynamics tells you how far you will go, while kinetics tells you how quickly you will get there. A classic example to illustrate this is the formation of graphite from diamond. Graphite and diamond are two of the several different forms (**allotropes**) of carbon, and the value of ΔG^o for the reaction $C_{(diamond)} \rightarrow C_{(graphite)}$ is about –2900 J/mol. Because ΔG^o is negative, the formation of graphite is favored under standard conditions, but it's *extremely* slow. Even diamond heirlooms passed down through many generations are still in diamond form.

Reversibility

Reactions follow the principle of microscopic reversibility: The reverse reaction has the same magnitude for all thermodynamic values (ΔG, ΔH, and ΔS) but of the opposite sign, and the same reaction pathway, but in reverse. This means that the reaction energy diagram for the reverse reaction can be drawn by simply using the mirror image of the forward reaction. The incongruity you should notice is that E_a is different for the forward and reverse reactions. Coming from the products side towards the reactants, the energy barrier will be the difference between $G_{products}$ and the energy of the activated complex.

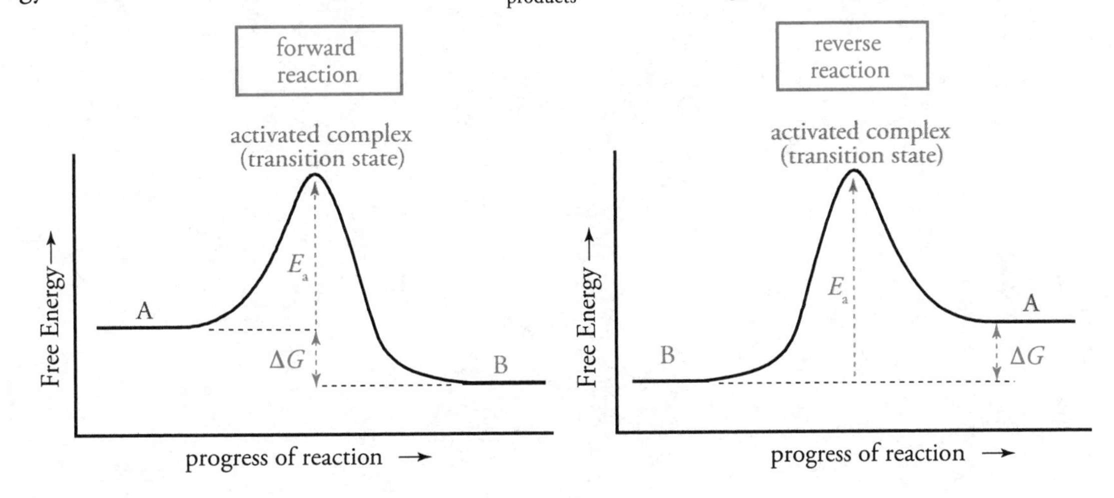

Chapter 6 Summary

- The Zeroth Law of Thermodynamics states that energy will flow from a body at a higher temperature to a body at a lower temperature until both bodies have the same temperature.
- Energy flow into a system has a positive sign. Energy flow out of a system has a negative sign.
- The First Law of Thermodynamics states that energy cannot be created or destroyed.
- The internal energy of an object is proportional to its temperature.
- The Second Law of Thermodynamics states that all processes tend toward maximum disorder, or entropy (S).
- Enthalpy (H) is a measure of the energy stored in the bonds of molecules.
- Breaking bonds requires energy ($+\Delta H$), while forming bonds releases energy ($-\Delta H$).
- Standard conditions are 1 atm and 298 K, 1 M concentrations. Standard conditions are denoted by a superscript "°".
- An endothermic reaction has a $\Delta H > 0$. An exothermic reaction has a $\Delta H < 0$.
- $\Delta H_{reaction} = H_{products} - H_{reactants}$. This equation can also be applied to ΔG and ΔS.
- ΔG, the Gibbs free energy, is the amount of energy in a reaction available to do chemical work.
- For a reaction under any set of conditions, $\Delta G = \Delta H - T\Delta S$.
- If $\Delta G < 0$, the reaction is spontaneous in the forward direction. If $\Delta G > 0$, the reaction is nonspontaneous in the forward direction. If $\Delta G = 0$, the reaction is at equilibrium.

CHAPTER 6 FREESTANDING PRACTICE QUESTIONS

1. During the electrolysis of liquid water into hydrogen and oxygen gas at standard temperature and pressure, energy is:

A) absorbed during the breaking of H—H bonds and the reaction is spontaneous.
B) released during the formation of H—H bonds and the reaction is nonspontaneous.
C) absorbed during the formation of O=O bonds and the reaction is spontaneous.
D) released during the breaking of O—H bonds and the reaction is nonspontaneous.

2. What could make the following nonspontaneous endothermic reaction spontaneous?

$$2\ H_2O(l) \rightarrow 2\ H_2(g) + O_2(g)$$

A) Decreasing volume
B) Increasing temperature
C) Decreasing temperature
D) The reaction will always be nonspontaneous.

3. Which of the following should have the highest enthalpy of vaporization?

A) N_2
B) Br_2
C) Hg
D) Al

4. A 36 gram sample of water requires 93.4 kJ to sublime. What are the heats of fusion (ΔH_{fus}) and vaporization (ΔH_{vap}) for water?

A) $\Delta H_{fus} = -20$ kJ/mol, $\Delta H_{vap} = 66.7$ kJ/mol
B) $\Delta H_{fus} = 40.7$ kJ/mol, $\Delta H_{vap} = 6.0$ kJ/mol
C) $\Delta H_{fus} = 6.0$ kJ/mol, $\Delta H_{vap} = 40.7$ kJ/mol
D) $\Delta H_{fus} = 12.0$ kJ/mol, $\Delta H_{vap} = 81.4$ kJ/mol

5. Given the standard enthalpies of formation (ΔH_f°) at 298 K for the compounds below, all of the following reactions are exothermic EXCEPT:

Compound	**ΔH_f° (kJ/mol)**
$C_2H_5OH(l)$	–238.86
$CH_3CHO(l)$	–77.80
$CH_3COOH(l)$	–484.50
$H_2O(l)$	–285.83

A) $CH_3COOH(l) \rightarrow CH_3CHO(l) + \frac{1}{2}\ O_2(g)$
B) $C_2H_5OH(l) + \frac{1}{2}\ O_2(g) \rightarrow CH_3CHO(l) + H_2O(l)$
C) $CH_3CHO(l) + \frac{1}{2}\ O_2(g) \rightarrow CH_3COOH(l)$
D) $C_2H_5OH(l) + O_2(g) \rightarrow CH_3COOH(l) + H_2O(l)$

6. The citric acid cycle consists of reactions that break down acetate into carbon dioxide. Given that some steps are thermodynamically unfavorable, why does the cycle proceed in the forward direction overall?

A) The rate constant for the unfavorable reactions is very large.
B) The cycle contains exergonic reactions that drive the endergonic reactions forward.
C) The endothermically unfavorable reactions also have a negative entropy change.
D) The activation energies of the unfavorable reactions are lowered by catalysts.

CHAPTER 6 PRACTICE PASSAGE

The extent to which a salt dissolves in water can be quantified by its solubility product constant, (K_{sp}) which is defined, for a hypothetical salt X_aY_b, as shown in Equation 2. The greater the value of K_{sp}, the more soluble the compound. The K_{sp} of a salt is related to the free energy of dissolution by the equation $\Delta G^o_{diss} = -RT\ln(K_{sp})$. Table 1 lists the K_{sp} values for some insoluble salts.

$$X_aY_b(s) \rightleftharpoons a\,X^{b+}(aq) + b\,Y^{a-}(aq)$$

Equation 1

$$K_{sp} = [X^{b+}]^a\,[Y^{a-}]^b$$

Equation 2

Salt	K_{sp}
$PbCl_2$	1.2×10^{-5}
$MgCO_3$	6.8×10^{-6}
$BaSO_4$	1.1×10^{-10}
AgCl	5.4×10^{-13}

Table 1 K_{sp} values for select insoluble salts

When a solid completely dissolves, solute particles are separated and encapsulated by solvent molecules. This process requires several steps: 1) breaking all solute-solute interactions, 2) disrupting some solvent-solvent interactions, and 3) forming new solute-solvent interactions. The combination of these processes determines the overall enthalpy change for the dissolution, which can be either exothermic or endothermic regardless of the solubility of the salt. Table 2 shows the enthalpies of dissolution for several soluble salts.

Salt	ΔH_{diss} (kJ/mol)
LiCl	–37.03
KCH_3CO_2	–15.33
NaCl	3.87
NH_4NO_3	25.69
$KClO_4$	41.38

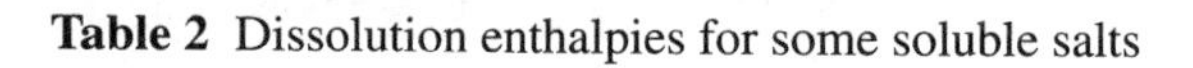

Table 2 Dissolution enthalpies for some soluble salts

As solids are low entropy materials, their dissolution entails an increase in entropy. The size of ΔS_{diss} is dependent on the organization of solvent molecules in the solvation sphere of the dissolved ions.

1. Which of the following species is isoelectronic with the silver ion in AgCl?

A) Rh^+
B) Pd
C) Cd^{2+}
D) In^-

2. Given that the dissolution of sodium chloride is spontaneous below the saturation concentration, which of the following statements must be true?

A) Forming solute-solvent interactions requires energy, while breaking solute-solute and solvent-solvent interactions releases energy.
B) The increase in entropy must outweigh the enthalpy change of dissolution to create a negative Gibbs free energy.
C) Sodium chloride is only soluble at high temperatures.
D) All ionically-bound materials are substantially soluble in water.

3. Which one of the salts in Table 1 has the smallest value of ΔG°_{diss}?

A) $PbCl_2$
B) $MgCO_3$
C) $BaSO_4$
D) AgCl

4. Which of the following is consistent with the differences in $\Delta H°_{diss}$ for NaCl and LiCl?

A) The electrostatic forces in solid LiCl are much stronger than in solid NaCl, while coordination of water is equivalent for both salts.
B) The electrostatic forces in the two solids are approximately equivalent, while water molecules coordinate much more effectively to Na^+ than Li^+.
C) The electrostatic forces in solid LiCl are weaker than in solid NaCl, while water cannot effectively coordinate to the very small Li^+ cation.
D) The electrostatic forces in solid NaCl are slightly weaker than in solid LiCl, while water far more efficiently coordinates Li^+ than Na^+.

5. The transfer of heat to or from a solution changes the temperature of the solution according to the equation $q = mc\Delta T$ where q is the heat transferred, m is the mass of solvent, and c is the specific heat of the solvent. If a 1 g sample of a salt was dissolved in 20 mL of water (specific heat = 4.18 J/g°C) in an insulated beaker and the temperature was found to decrease by 4°C, which of the following salts was used? Assume no phase change for the water.

A) LiCl
B) KCH_3CO_2
C) NH_4NO_3
D) NaCl

SOLUTIONS TO CHAPTER 6 FREESTANDING PRACTICE QUESTIONS

1. **B** Electrolysis requires energy. Water will not split into hydrogen and oxygen gas spontaneously at standard temperature and pressure which eliminates choices A and C. When bonds are broken, energy is absorbed (eliminates choice D). Energy is released when bonds are formed.

2. **B** Choice A is eliminated because decreasing volume would cause an increase in pressure, which would inhibit the transformation of a liquid to a gas. The question alludes that the process has a positive ΔH. Since the reaction involves changing two moles of liquid to three moles of gas, entropy increases so it will have a positive ΔS. Using the equation $\Delta G = \Delta H\ T\Delta S$, a reaction with a positive ΔH and ΔS will be spontaneous only at high enough temperatures. Therefore, choices C and D can be eliminated, making choice B correct.

3. **D** Enthalpy of vaporization is the heat energy required per mole to change from the liquid to gas phase. N_2 is a gas at room temperature, Br_2 and Hg are both liquids at room temperature, and Al is a solid at room temperature. Therefore, it is expected that Al will have the highest enthalpy of vaporization, making choice D correct.

4. **C** Both fusion (melting) and vaporization (boiling) require energy and are endothermic, eliminating choice A. Comparing both processes, vaporization takes substantially more energy. During vaporization, intermolecular forces are essentially completely overcome, and gaseous molecules separate widely due to their increased kinetic energy. Choice B is therefore eliminated. A 36 gram sample of water is 2 moles, so the heat of sublimation of 1 mole is half of 93.4 kJ, or 46.7 kJ/mol. This eliminates choice D. Examining the fusion and vaporization of water and adding their enthalpies by Hess's law gives choice C as the correct answer:

$$H_2O(s) \rightarrow H_2O(l) \qquad \Delta H_{fus} = X\ (6.0\ \text{kJ/mol})$$

$$H_2O(l) \rightarrow H_2O(g) \qquad \Delta H_{vap} = Y\ (40.7\ \text{kJ/mol})$$

$$H_2O(s) \rightarrow H_2O(g) \qquad \Delta H_{vap} = X + Y = 46.7\ \text{kJ/mol}$$

5. **A** The change in enthalpy (ΔH) for a reaction is equal to the sum of $\Delta H_f°$ for products minus the sum of $\Delta H_f°$ for reactants: $\Delta H = \Sigma\ \Delta H_{f\ (products)} - \Sigma\ \Delta H_{f\ (reactants)}$. For choice A, the lone reduction reaction, ΔH = (–77.8 kJ/mol) – (–484.50 kJ/mol). This is a positive value indicating that enthalpy is absorbed and the reaction is endothermic. Note that the heat of formation of diatomic oxygen gas or any element in its naturally occurring form is defined as 0. The other answer choices, which are all oxidation reactions, will yield a negative value indicating they are exothermic.

6. **B** The question is asking about thermodynamic principles, so answer choices A and D that involve kinetics can be eliminated. Reactions with a positive ΔH and a negative ΔS are never spontaneous according to $\Delta G = \Delta H - T\Delta S$, eliminating choice C. If the sum of all reactions is more exergonic ($-\Delta G$) than endergonic ($+\Delta G$), the net release of free energy will drive the cycle forward, making choice B the best answer.

SOLUTIONS TO CHAPTER 6 PRACTICE PASSAGE

1. **C** Isoelectronic species have the same electron configurations, and hence the same number of electrons. Ag^+ has 46 electrons, eliminating choices A and D because they have 44 and 50 electrons, respectively. The electron configuration of Ag^+ is [Kr] $4d^{10}$. The electron configuration of Pd is [Kr] $5s^2 3d^8$ (eliminate choice B). The electron configuration of Cd^{2+} is [Kr] $4d^{10}$, which is isoelectronic with Ag^+.

2. **B** Similar to bond formation, forming solute-solvent interactions is exothermic, meaning energy is released, not required; similarly breaking solute-solute or solvent-solvent interactions is endothermic (requires energy), like bond breaking (eliminate choice A). In addition, sodium chloride is soluble at room temperature (eliminate choice C). Salts are held together by ionic bonds, but Table 1 shows through the small K_{sp} values that not all of them are substantially soluble (eliminate choice D). For the dissolution of sodium chloride to be spontaneous, the increase in entropy must outweigh the endothermic process (note that NaCl has a positive enthalpy of dissolution from Table 2), yielding a negative Gibbs free energy.

3. **A** The important relationship between the standard state Gibbs free energy of dissolution and the solubility product constant is given in the passage:

$$\Delta G^\circ_{diss} = -RT\ln K_{sp}$$

Since the question asks for an extreme, first eliminate the two choices for K_{sp} in Table 1 that are the middle values (choices B and C). The ln function is similar to the log function, and can be thought of in the same way when judging relative magnitudes of ΔG°_{diss} in the equation above. For values of $K_{sp} > 1$, the ΔG° value will be negative, and for values of $K_{sp} < 1$, the ΔG° value will be positive. Therefore, the larger value of K_{sp} for $PbCl_2$ will give the smallest value for ΔG°.

4. **D** Effective dissolution involves the endothermic step of overcoming the electrostatic charges holding the solid salts together and the exothermic step of coordinating solvents to the separated ions. A negative value of ΔH°_{diss} likely indicates relatively weak electrostatic forces in the solid (small endothermic step), and effective solvation by water (large exothermic step). Table 2 shows that LiCl has a much more negative value of ΔH°_{diss} than NaCl. Choice A, stronger electrostatic forces in LiCl and no difference in solvation, would lead to a more negative ΔH°_{diss} for NaCl. Choice B would also result in a more negative value of ΔH°_{diss} for NaCl, as it indicates that electrostatics are equivalent while Na^+ has stronger interactions with water. Choice C is incorrect because a large negative value of ΔH°_{diss} would be difficult to achieve if water were unable to coordinate Li^+. Choice D includes a viable combination of slightly weaker attractive forces in NaCl but much better solvation for Li^+.

5. C Since the question states that the temperature of the solution decreased, the salts with exothermic dissolution enthalpies (choices A and B) can be eliminated. Using the calorimetry equation given in the question stem ($q = mc\Delta T$), we can estimate:

$$20 \text{ g} \times \approx 4 \text{ J/g°C} \times 4\text{°C} = \approx 320 \text{ J} = \approx 0.32 \text{ kJ} = q$$

Since this heat is associated with 1 g of salt, in order to compare to the $\Delta H°_{\text{diss}}$ in Table 2, convert this energy to a per mole basis by multiplying by the molar mass of the salt.

For choice C (NH_4NO_3, MW = 80 g/mol), this yields:

$$\approx 0.3 \text{ kJ/1 g } NH_4NO_3 \times 80 \text{ g } NH_4NO_3\text{/mol} = 24 \text{ kJ/mol}$$

which is close to the given 25.69 kJ/mol in the table. The comparable calculation for NaCl yields:

$$\approx 0.3 \text{ kJ/1 g NaCl} \times \approx 60 \text{ g NaCl/mol} = 18 \text{ kJ/mol}$$

so choice D can be eliminated.